Minia
Railv

Second Edition

Robin Butterell   Dave Holroyde   Simon Townsend

Ian Allan PUBLISHING

Contents

Front cover, upper:
No 5751 Prince William *seen raising steam at the Windmill Animal Farm Railway on 13 June 1999.* Dave Holroyde

Front cover, lower:
At the 12¼in gauge Nickelodeon line at Ashorne Hall in Warwickshire, 2-4-2T Ashorne *was photographed working a demonstration train soon after its delivery to the railway in 1994.* Dave Holroyde

Back cover:
A busy scene at Upsan Downs terminus on the Beer Heights Light Railway, 7¼in gauge, during the Pecorama 1999 Steam and Model Festival on 12 June.
Simon Townsend

First published 2000

ISBN 0 7110 2713 7

Published by Ian Allan Publishing

an imprint of Ian Allan Publishing Ltd, Terminal House, Shepperton, Surrey TW17 8AS.
Printed by Ian Allan Printing Ltd, Riverdene Business Park, Hersham, Surrey KT12 4RG.

Code: 0004/B2

INTRODUCTION
to the Second Edition

In this book we have endeavoured to include details of all commercial miniature railways that will be open to the public during 2000, from 21in gauge down to 7¼ in gauge.

Of course, all miniature railways are narrow gauge railways but the converse is not necessarily true. Many of the miniature railways in this book have locomotives (and sometimes rolling stock) which are models of real or imaginary prototypes of larger or standard gauge types. Even so, some of the lines are genuinely 'minimum gauge railways', doing jobs of work in their own right, without direct inspiration from larger ancestors.

We were pleased to find that our modest effort of two years ago was sufficiently popular in our modern world to warrant the commissioning of this second edition. We have updated all the facts and figures as fully as we can, largely from the records kept by Dave Holroyde, who is Miniature Lines Records Officer for the Narrow Gauge Railway Society. In this edition we have promoted quite a few society-operated 'club tracks' to the main section of the book. We have tried to give full details of those club tracks which open most regularly to the public, the remainder being summarised at the back of the book. We have also added addresses for those railways that have websites on the Internet.

We would like to thank all the miniature railway operators who contributed information for this book. We should also acknowledge the help of Peter Scott, whose series of 'Track Plans of Minor Railways' published by the Kentrail Enthusiasts Group (34 Meadow Road, Earley, Reading RG6 7EX) has been a great help to us in writing descriptions of each location. We have taken every step we can to ensure accuracy of the information; any errors which may have occurred can be advised to us c/o the publisher.

The miniature railway, decades after the disappearance of main line steam, now occupies an important role in the overall scene for the railway enthusiast, with many superb and high quality layouts all over the United Kingdom to delight the discerning enthusiast and members of the general public.

0-6-4T Zebedee *hauling its train around the balloon loop at East Wheal Rose on the Lappa Valley Railway, 23 August 1998.* Dave Holroyde

STANDARD ABBREVIATIONS

Addresses
These are in all cases the addresses of the railways concerned, rather than being postal addresses of the railways' operators. We have endeavoured to reflect county boundaries as at April 1998. In case you find some of these new areas confusing, we have added some of the former counties in brackets.

Telephone Numbers
Where given, these are generally numbers of the location concerned. In a small number of cases the railway operators have permitted us to publish their home phone numbers; these are marked (H). Please do not abuse these by calling at irregular hours.

Operators
Wherever known, these are the individuals or companies responsible for running trains, not necessarily the land or stock owners, or, in the case of companies, the company owners.

Websites
During the lifetime of this book no doubt a good number of additional railways will gain websites, and some of the existing sites will change their URL addresses. If you are new to the Internet we recommend http://www.users.globalnet.co.uk/~stownsen or http://freespace.virgin.net/ian.thomas1 as good starting points for miniature railway subjects.

Line Lengths
These are approximate, to the nearest 50yd.

Layouts

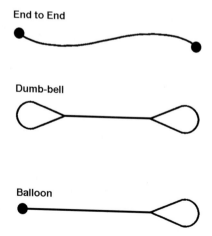

End to End

Dumb-bell

Balloon

First Opened
These are the years of the first miniature railway presence on site, not necessarily of the same gauge or necessarily implying continuous service since.

Locomotive Numbers and Names
These are shown as carried on the locomotives concerned; those not carried are denoted in brackets.

Type
Steam: The 'Whyte' notation of wheel arrangements has been used: ST — saddle tank; T — side tank; VB — vertical boiler; WT — well tank.

Internal Combustion: w indicates powered axle, for instance, 4-4w means two four-wheeled bogies, rear bogie powered on all four wheels. 'Whyte' notation is used where transmission is by outside connecting rods, eg 0-4-2DM. S/O — steam outline; BE — battery electric; BER — battery-electric railcar; DE — diesel electric; DER — diesel-electric railcar; DH — diesel hydraulic; DHR — diesel-hydraulic railcar; GasH — gas hydraulic; DM — diesel mechanical: PM — petrol mechanical; PMR — petrol-mechanical railcar; PH — petrol hydraulic; RE— electric, power from third rail; WER — overhead-wire electric railcar.

Builder
Company names have been abbreviated, eg Severn Lamb Ltd to just Severn Lamb. In some cases trading names have been used for individuals or partnerships.

Opening Hours
It would be impossible for us to include detailed opening hours of each location, as they would be lengthy and subject to change. We have, however, included some details where they are unusual, for instance one day a week. Some lines operate all year round, particularly those which are near to major centres of population rather than in seaside areas or amusement parks. Some railways only open weather permitting; one operator wrote this and then said 'but it has to be pretty bad to stop us'; brave man! In virtually all cases fine Sundays during the summer school holidays are the best times to find miniature railways busy. If at all in doubt, telephone or write before travelling to visit a specific railway.

Photography and Other Matters
Miniature lines offer much for the railway photographer; trains are frequent and there is immense variety between the different locations. Always start your visit by riding round on the train. It's the best way to see all the locations on offer, and to give something to the humble operator. Always gain permission before crossing fences or entering the shed area. If the other locomotives are locked up, don't expect a guided tour in mid-afternoon; first thing or last thing are generally the best times.

Many operators of railways in this book are enthusiasts themselves to some extent, but the view from the footplate can be surprisingly different to that of the visitor. If you travel 150 miles on a wet Tuesday in June to find the railway deserted or the steam engine broken, don't blame us, we're just the authors. If on the other hand you have an enjoyable time, then mention *abc Miniature Railways* and say we sent you!

Disclaimer
The information contained in this publication has been published in good faith and every effort has been made to ensure its accuracy. Neither the publisher nor the authors can accept any responsibility for any error or misinterpretation. All liability for loss, disappointment, negligence or other damage caused by reliance on the information contained in this publication, or in respect of facilities for the disabled, or in the event of any bankruptcy or liquidation or cessation of the trade of any company, individual or firm mentioned, is hereby excluded.

Models have been made by man from time immemorial, either to show how a finished object would look when constructed, or for the fascination and satisfaction of showing the object in a smaller scale when complete. Alongside early model builders there came Sir Arthur Percival Heywood. Sir Arthur believed that railways as small as 15in gauge could perform a useful job of work. He built his first locomotive in 1875, and with it a spectacular railway which climbed up the hill behind his house at Duffield in Derbyshire. Publication of his book *Minimum Gauge Railways* led in 1896 to the construction of a second, longer, railway for the Duke of Westminster at Eaton Hall in Cheshire. Other than this, one could say that Sir Arthur's ideas never really caught on in his lifetime, but today his name is revered as the founder of small railways designed in their own right, rather than as models. It has been a pleasure recently to find that full-sized replicas have been built of several of Heywood's locomotives.

It was the Cagney Brothers in the USA who first exploited the notion of small railways as pleasure attractions. When a few of their train sets arrived over here, they led W. J. Bassett-Lowke and Henry Greenly to think that they too could build miniature railways. Bassett-Lowke was an astute businessman who came to be the doyen of the model railway world; Greenly was a brilliant designer whose legacy may still be seen at many of the locations in this book. In 1905 Bassett-Lowke's works at Northampton built a 15in gauge 4-4-2 named *Little Giant*, of broadly scale appearance. By 1910 Bassett-Lowke could supply equipment in 7¼in, 9½in and 15in gauges. Whatever the customer wanted, from castings and drawings to complete railways, they continued to sell right up to 1939.

In 1915 Bassett-Lowke took over an abandoned 3ft gauge line on the Cumbrian coast at Ravenglass, and relaid the 7-mile track to 15in gauge. The Ravenglass & Eskdale Railway operated continuously until taken over by a preservation society in 1960, from when it has gone from strength to strength. Henry Greenly's ultimate achievement came in 1927 with the design of the Romney, Hythe & Dymchurch Railway. Conceived by its owner Jack Howey as a main line in miniature, in due course it stretched for 14 miles along the low-lying Romney marshes in Kent from Hythe to Dungeness, a shingle promontory which juts out into the English Channel. Here most of the locomotives were modelled on London & North Eastern Railway Pacifics, but to the ⅓ scale, giving an impressive appearance. They are all still operating today, some 70 years on.

9½in gauge was never as popular, because by 1910 the virtues of 10¼in gauge had already been proven and well publicised. The Surrey Border & Camberley Railway, running from Farnborough to Camberley, was the most ambitious 10¼in gauge railway ever built; alas it closed in 1939.

With the return to normal conditions in 1945, leisure attractions again became popular and miniature railways, some of which had been 'mothballed' for the duration, opened up again. A considerable number of new lines were built. With them came a new generation of designers and builders, such as David Curwen, who has been designing and building miniature locomotives on and off since 1946, most recently for the 10¼in gauge railway at Audley End.

From 1967 the firm of Severn Lamb enjoyed a period of dominance in the market for heavily built railway equipment for commercial railway operators. Steam outline i/c (internal combustion) locomotives have been a particular speciality, and their 'Rio Grande' steam outline 2-8-0s and 2-6-0s operate, often unassisted, at many locations in this book.

Two 7¼in gauge railways, the Greywood Central Railway and the Hilton Valley Railway, particularly paved the way for future developments. Following the death of its owner the Greywood Central Railway was, from 1965, progressively re-established as the Great

No 6100 Royal Scot *pauses at Cockcrow Hill whilst working a down branch train from Hardwick Central, 7 June 1998.* N. R. Knight

Cockcrow Railway near Chertsey. Here, scale models of British standard gauge prototypes reign supreme, in an extremely intensive and professional operation. By way of contrast, the Hilton Valley Railway, near Bridgnorth, moved far beyond the concepts of 'scale', with some very heavy and durable stock and locomotives being built. The HVR closed in 1979, following the death of its owner Michael Lloyd.

In 1968 Roger Marsh designed and built *Tinkerbell,* a 7¼in 0-4-2T which the driver sits in rather than on. A batch of these were built at his Hinckley works, and were followed by other designs easy enough for the home builder, for which castings are still being sold. In 1973 the 7¼in Gauge Society was founded, and model engineers began building equipment for ground level 7¼in gauge railways in ever greater numbers. Some enthusiasts who built 7¼in gauge lines for their own pleasure found that they naturally attracted visitors and, with a bit of extra effort, could be opened to the public commercially. The Forest Railway at Dobwalls started this way, one of the first of many in this book.

Most miniature railway vehicles strike a balance between dimensions, weight, capacity and stability. It is just about possible on 7¼in gauge vehicles for passengers and driver to sit inside their trains. Some 10¼in gauge vehicles can seat two adults side by side, but sometimes only if you get to know your neighbour well! Most 7¼in gauge passenger vehicles are 'sit astride' types, which have high capacity for a given weight. Some of the latest 15in gauge vehicles seat three adults side by side.

John Ellerton found another permutation when he commissioned four half-size 2ft gauge locomotives for 12¼in gauge; these now run at Fairbourne. The Exmoor Steam Railway has been a notable builder in 12¼in gauge. The most recent locomotives built there (both for themselves and for customers such as the 15in gauge lines at Perrygrove and Markeaton Park) are true minimum gauge machines.

By visiting a balanced selection of, say, 10 or 20 miniature railways you can expect to see strands of history from most of the developments above. There are enthusiasts sharing their hobby by running public trains hauled by scale models. There are those continually exploring the concept of 'minimum gauge', and amusement park operators who just want trains that are economic to run and look OK to a six year old. There are 'basic' lines, and others that have gone to great trouble building lineside accessories, such as signals, level crossings, platforms and station buildings. There are lines opened 50 or 80 years ago, and others that are brand new; and an equally colourful mix of locomotives. It's a fascinating world, which we hope this book will encourage you to explore.

AREA 1: SOUTH WEST

Bath & North East Somerset, Bristol, Cornwall, Devon, Dorset, North Somerset, Somerset, Wiltshire.

BEER HEIGHTS LIGHT RAILWAY

7¼in gauge

Pecorama Pleasure Gardens and Exhibition, Underlys, Beer, nr Seaton, Devon EX12 3NA
Telephone: 01297 21542   *OS Ref:* SY224893   *Operator:* Howe & Davis Ltd
Website: http://www.peco-uk.com/pecorama.htm
Line length: 1,300yd, complex   *First opened:* 1975   Park entry fee

No	Name	Type	Builder	Built
5	Linda	2-4-0ST	J. Clarke	1971
3	Dickie	0-4-2	D. Curwen	1976
4	Thomas II	0-4-2ST	R. Marsh	1979
7	Mr P	2-4-2	BHLR	1997
8	Gem	0-6-0T+T	Demslow/BHLR	1998
6	Jimmy	4-4wDH	Severn Lamb	1986

This line is built high on a hill with deep cuttings, high embankments and a long tunnel under the car park. Immaculately maintained with full signalling and realistic lineside buildings, the railway is one of the finest in the country. Pecorama is closed on Saturday afternoons, except on bank holiday weekends.

BICKINGTON STEAM RAILWAY

10¼in gauge

Trago Mills Shopping & Leisure Centre, Stover, nr Newton Abbot, Devon TQ12 6JB
Telephone: 01626 821111   *OS Ref:* SX821742   *Operator:* Trago Mills
Line length: 1 mile   *First opened:* 1988

No	Name	Type	Builder	Built
750	Blanche of Lancaster	4-4-2	D. Curwen	1948
1	E. R. Calthrop	2-6-4T	Coleby Simkins	1974
	Alice	2-6-0	Simkins & Vere	1984
24	(Sandy River)	2-6-2	Clarkson/Vere & Nicholson	1991
D5905	IXL	4w-4wDH	D. Nicholson	1987

This line has an imposing main station at Trago Central, from where trains descend over a 23-pier viaduct, before looping round across themselves several times and then climbing back again. At one point there are six parallel tracks all on different levels. *E. R. Calthrop* is a model of a 2ft 6in gauge loco which once ran on the Leek & Manifold Railway in Staffordshire. *Blanche of Lancaster* once achieved fame by appearing on TV in an episode of 'The Avengers', filmed at the Stapleford Miniature Railway.

BLAISE CASTLE MINIATURE RAILWAY

15in gauge

Blaise Castle, Henbury, Bristol BS10 7QS
Telephone: (H): 01275 872670   *OS Ref:* ST559786   *Operator:* R. Giles
Line length: 300yd, end to end   *First opened:* 1974

No	Name	Type	Builder	Built
2	Goram	2w-2-4BER	Hayne/Minirail	1977
1	Vincent	2w-2-4BER	Hayne/Minirail	1983

A charming if idiosyncratic line, popular with children visiting the Blaise Castle estate. Both railcars were originally coaches, much modified by Norman Hayne (the line's previous owner) using milk float technology to provide traction. They are now named after giants who, as legend has it, once roamed the estate.

BREAN CENTRAL MINIATURE RAILWAY
7¼in gauge

Brean Leisure Park, Coast Road, Brean, Somerset TA8 2QY
Telephone: 01278 751595   *OS Ref:* ST296544   *Operator:* J. Colishaw
Line length: 250yd, circular   *First opened:* 1973

No	Name	Type	Builder	Built
6691		4-4wPH	R. Greatrex	1986

A short line encircling this small amusement park, passing through the tunnel/shed as it goes.

BUCKFASTLEIGH MINIATURE RAILWAY
7¼in gauge

South Devon Railway Station, Buckfastleigh, Devon TQ11 0DZ
Telephone: 01364 642338   *OS Ref:* SX747663
Operator: Torbay & District Miniature Railway Society
Line length: 750yd, circular   *First opened:* 1977

No	Name	Type	Builder	Built
	William	0-4-0T	W. Manley	c1974
	Roy Owen	0-4-0ST	D. Bussey	1983
		0-4-0	C. Elliott	1999
	Romulus	0-4-0	Corder/Cooper	1999
		2-4-0	P. Winsor	1999
	Bob	0-6-0PH	G. Cooper	1995
		0-4-0PH	G. Cooper	1998
	Jo-Jo	0-4-0PH	Roanoke	1998

This railway runs around the picnic area behind the locomotive shed at the South Devon Railway. Several lines here have come and gone before this one; 2-6-2T *Yeo* operated here before moving on when the Gorse Blossom Miniature Railway Park opened.

CLEVEDON MINIATURE RAILWAY
9½in gauge

Salthouse Fields, Clevedon, North Somerset BS21 7XP
Telephone (H): 01275 872670   *OS Ref:* ST398710   *Operator:* A. Giles
Line length: 900yd, circular   *First opened:* 1952

No	Name	Type	Builder	Built
595	Charles Henry	S/O 2-8-0PH	Severn Lamb	1976

This locomotive is the smallest gauge of Severn Lamb 'Rio Grande' yet built; 595 was its owner's number before his retirement from the police service. The circuit runs around an open field; steam once operated here many years ago.

COMBE MARTIN WILDLIFE PARK RAILWAY   *15in gauge*

Combe Martin Wildlife & Dinosaur Park, Higher Leigh, Combe Martin, Devon EX34 0NG
Telephone: 01271 882486   *OS Ref:* SS600452   *Operator:* Mr Butcher
Line length: 500yd, end to end   *First opened:* 1989   Park entry fee

No	Name	Type	Builder	Built
		S/O 2-8-0PH	Severn Lamb	1987

An end to end run with a station, tunnel, and bridge over a stream.

CRICKET ST THOMAS RAILWAY   *15in gauge*

The Wildlife Park at Cricket St Thomas, nr Chard, Somerset TA20 4DD
Telephone: 01460 30111   *OS Ref:* ST376086   *Operator:* Warner Holidays
Line length: 800yd, end to end   *First opened:* 1975   Park entry fee

No	Name	Type	Builder	Built
		4w-4wDH	G&SLE	1957
		S/O 0-6-2DH	Alan Keef	1995

This line runs from Lemur Wood station, along the side of a valley and through animal enclosures, before swinging round over a substantial viaduct to terminate at Flamingo Junction. It is possible to run both trains, passing at a loop halfway along the track. The run round loops at the termini have recently been lifted, as both rakes of stock can now be driven from driving trailers whilst being propelled.

The 4w-4wDH locomotive stands with its train in the passing loop at the Cricket St Thomas Railway in October 1998. Pat Henshaw

Dobwalls, nr Liskeard, Cornwall PL14 6HD
Telephone: 01579 320325 *OS Ref:* SX213658 *Operator:* Forest Railways Ltd
Website: http://www.chycor.co.uk/tourism/cata/dobwalls-fap/dobwalls-fap.htm
Rio Grande Railroad: 1,300yd, circular; *Union Pacific Railroad:* 900yd, circular
First opened: 1970 Park entry fee

No	Name	Type	Builder	Built
488	General Palmer	2-8-2	D. Curwen	1971
8	David Curwen	2-6-2	D. Curwen	1972
818	Queen of Wyoming	4-8-4	Severn Lamb	1974
X4008	William Jeffers	4-8-8-4	Severn Lamb	1978
498	Otto Mears	2-8-2	D. Curwen	1980
838	Queen of Nebraska	4-8-4	Severn Lamb	1981
6908	Centennial	8w-8DH	Severn Lamb	1979
3008	Mathias Baldwin	4w-4DH	Severn Lamb	1980
248	Spirit of America	6-6+6w-6wDH	Severn Lamb	1983
5908	Pioneer	6w-6wDH	Severn Lamb	1989

'Circular' is technically correct but hardly does justice to the two routes of the Forest Railroads, which twist and climb around, under and over themselves, passing landmarks of their full-sized counterparts as they go. *William Jeffers* is a model of the UP 'Big Boy' class, and really is a sight in itself. If you haven't already been, you will find that these railroads have a high 'aah' factor. Recent practice has been to operate one route using steam and the other using diesel, on each day.

An impressive machine by any standards is 4-8-8-4 William Jeffers, *seen here in the arrivals platform of the Union Pacific route at the Dobwalls Family Adventure Park.*
Robin Butterell

EXMOOR STEAM RAILWAY

Cape of Good Hope Farm, Bratton Fleming, Devon EX32 7SN
Telephone: 01598 710711   *OS Ref:* SS661382
Operators: T. Stirland & family
Line length: 1,100yd, end to end   *First opened:* 1990   Park entry fee

No	Name	Type	Builder	Built
299	Denzil	0-4-2T	Exmoor Steam Railway	1995
296		2-4-2T	Exmoor Steam Railway	1998
		0-4-2T	Exmoor Steam Railway	2000
		0-4-2T	Exmoor Steam Railway	2000

Since this location first opened to the public, developments and improvements have been made continually, the latest being the opening of a new terminus named 'Cape of Good Hope'. Trains now run round here, before returning round the spiral section to Exmoor Central. This is very much a 'minimum gauge' railway; the Stirlands' expertise is such that they have supplied a number of steam locomotives for other lines. An 0-4-2T and a Meyer are under construction. Five large 2ft gauge locomotives from South Africa are on static display here.

EXMOUTH EXPRESS

Exmouth Fun Park, Marine Drive, Exmouth, Devon
OS Ref: SY003804
Line length: 150yd, circular   *First opened:* 1949

No	Name	Type	Builder	Built
		4wDM	G. M. Kichenside	1978

A short circuit forming part of the sea front amusements; the line passes through the stock shed en route.

GORSE BLOSSOM MINIATURE RAILWAY & WOODLAND PARK

Gorse Blossom Farm, Liverton, Newton Abbot, Devon TQ12 6JD
Telephone: 01626 821361   *OS Ref:* SX815740
Operators: M. & B. Gottlieb
Website: http://www.gorseblossom.com
Line length: 1,500yd, circular   *First opened:* 1984   Park entry fee

No	Name	Type	Builder	Built
	Yeo	2-6-2T	Milner Engineering	1979
615	Klosters	4w-4wBE	Pfeifferbahn	1990
	Pegasus	4-4wBE	W. Baker	c1982
2	Heidi	4wBE	Cromar White	1976

Yeo and *Klosters* take their passengers for a ride in and out of the woodlands, through tunnels and over a girder bridge; it is not easy to work out where you're going next. There is also a separate double-track circuit 100yd long, around which visitors can drive the two smaller locos themselves. This encircles an ambitious 'G' scale railway based on the Rhaetian Railway main line between Solis and Preda. Trains to ride on, trains to look at, and a train you can drive yourself!

HUNTERS REST MINIATURE RAILWAY   *7¼in gauge*

Hunters Rest Public House, King Lane, Clutton Hill, nr Temple Cloud, Bath & North East Somerset BS39 5QL
Telephone: 01761 452303   *OS Ref:* ST633601   *Operator:* M. Pearce
Line length: 500yd, circular   *First opened:* 1984

No	Name	Type	Builder	Built
	Johnathan	0-4-0ST	J. Woodroofe	c1985
	Taurus	4w-4PH	Mardyke	c1983

A steeply graded layout at the back of this public house, including a double-track station and tunnel. The line runs through deep cuttings around Blackberry Hill, and adjacent to the small lake.

JUNGLE EXPRESS   *10¼in gauge*

Paignton Zoo Environmental Park, Totnes Road, Paignton, Torbay, Devon TQ4 7EU
Telephone: 01803 697500   *OS Ref:* SX878576
Operator: Whitley Wildlife Conservation Trust
Line length: 500yd, circular   *First opened:* 1937   Zoo entry fee

No	Name	Type	Builder	Built
		4-4wPM	G&SLE	1939
37401		4-4wDM	Nicholson/Wedgewood	1995

This long-established line has its station at the side of the main pathway through the zoo. It runs around the adjacent lake and over two bridges.

LAPPA VALLEY STEAM RAILWAY   *15in, and also 7¼in and 10¼in gauges*

St Newlyn East, Newquay, Cornwall TR8 5HZ
Telephone: 01872 510317   *OS Ref:* SW839573
Operator: Lappa Valley Railway Co Ltd
Website: http://www.chycor.co.uk/lappa-valley-railway
15in gauge: 1¼ miles, balloon   *First opened:* 1974
Newlyn Branch line; *10¼in gauge:* 700yd, end to end   *First opened:* 1995
Woodland Railway; *7¼in gauge:* 300yd, circular   *First opened:* 1978

No	Name	Type	Builder	Built
15in gauge:				
No 2	Muffin	0-6-0	Berwyn Engineering	1967
No 1	Zebedee	0-6-4T	Severn Lamb	1974
No 4	Pooh	4wDM	Lister	1942
	Gladiator	4-4wDH	Minirail	1960
10¼in gauge:				
	Duke of Cornwall	4w-4PH	Severn Lamb	1981
7¼in gauge:				
		4w+4wPH	Mardyke	1987

This is the only location in this book where you can ride upon three different gauges of miniature railway. The 15in gauge takes you from the car park at Benny Halt to East Wheal Rose, where there is an historic mine engine house along with a boating lake and other attractions. From there, included in the one charge, you can travel further along the standard gauge trackbed using the 10¼in gauge line, or with the kiddies whizz round in circles in a sit-in 'APT' set on the 7¼in gauge. Founded by Eric Booth, this popular attraction is now owned and operated by his family. Watch out for some interesting technical features, like the cross between a turntable and a sector plate at Benny Halt.

LITTLE WESTERN RAILWAY
7¼in gauge

Trenance Gardens, Newquay, Cornwall
Telephone: 01872 510317   *OS Ref:* SW819614   *Operator:* E. Booth
Line length: 300yd, circular   *First opened:* c1965

No	Name	Type	Builder	Built
33	Jinty	4wPM	A. Henwood	1979
Y054		4-4wPH	Mardyke	1980
1005		4-4wPH	Mardyke	1983

This attractive little line is normally operated by a Mardyke 'HST' set. No 1005 is the spare loco for here and the line at East Wheal Rose.

LONGLEAT RAILWAY
15in gauge

Longleat House, Warminster, Wiltshire BA12 7NW
Telephone: 01985 844400   *OS Ref:* ST808432   *Operator:* J. Hayton
Website: http://www.longleat.co.uk/
Line length: 1 mile, balloon   *First opened:* 1965   Park entry fee

No	Name	Type	Builder	Built
3	Dougal	0-6-2T	Severn Lamb	1970
5	Ceawlin	S/O 2-8-2DH	Severn Lamb/Hayton	1975
4	Lenka	4+4wDHR	J. Hayton	1984

Situated adjoining the well-known stately home of Lord Bath, the line runs from Longleat Central station through parkland and alongside a lake for half a mile, where sea lions and monkeys can be seen on an island. Hippos sometimes surface. A busy, well-established line.

MOORS VALLEY RAILWAY
7¼in gauge

Moors Valley Country Park, Horton Road, Ashley Heath, nr Ringwood, Dorset BH24 2ET
Telephone: 01425 471415   *OS Ref:* SU104060   *Operator:* Narogauge Ltd
Website: http://www.angelfire.com/mo/mvrlinks
Line length: 2,000yd, complex   *First opened:* 1986

No	Name	Type	Builder	Built
(4)	Tinkerbell	0-4-2T	R. Marsh	1968
(3)	Talos	0-4-2T	R. Marsh	1978
1	Sir Goss	2-4-0	J. Goss	1981
6	Medea	2-6-2T	J. Haylock/M. Sharp/J. Goss	1981
(5)	Sapper	4-6-0	R. Marsh/J. Haylock	1982
7	Aelfred	2-6-4T	Tuckton	1985
9	Jason	2-4-4T	Moors Valley Railway	1989
10	Offa	2-6-2	Moors Valley Railway	1991
11	Zeus	2-6-2	A. Culver/Moors Valley Railway	1991
(14)	Horton	2-4-0	Moors Valley Railway	1991

At Kingsmere station on the Moors Valley Railway, Garratt William Rufus *is at the head of a special train, whilst to the left* Sapper *stands in the arrivals platform, 11 October 1998.* Simon Townsend

12	Pioneer	4-6-2	Moors Valley Railway	1992
(13)	Tiny Tim	0-4-0T	Moors Valley Railway	1993
(15)	William Rufus	2-4-0+0-4-2T	Moors Valley Railway	1996
16	Robert Snooks	0-4-4T	Manktelow/Berriman	1999
17	Hartfield	2-4-4T	M. Colbourne	1999
2		0-4-2DH	Moors Valley Railway	1999

Conceived as a small gauge railway capable of carrying 150,000 passengers per year, the Moors Valley is really in a class of its own. It all started when Roger Marsh built *Tinkerbell*, which was the first 7¼in gauge locomotive one sat in, rather than on. From this basic theme Jim Haylock has developed the railway's impressive stud of minimum gauge locomotives, capable of hauling heavy trains around the steep gradients and sharp curves of this line, particularly where it spirals around the adventure playground.

When the railway moved here from Tucktonia in 1985, what is now Kingsmere station was the hub of a dairy farm. Now the buildings form a four-platform enclosed station, carriage shed, workshop, loco shed and shop. Movements are controlled from two signalboxes, that at Kingsmere having the lever frame formerly installed at Beckton Gas Works in East London. Although basically a circuit, passengers normally travel over the line in two journeys, detraining at Kingsmere whilst the train draws into the headshunt and then back into a departure road. On Sundays only throughout the year a special train, the 'Midday Limited', departs for a nonstop run (signals permitting) twice around the circuit, once in each direction. On peak days there is also a shuttle train between Lakeside and Kingsmere stations. Regular special events are held.

It might be 7¼in gauge, but the Moors Valley is a complete railway in every sense.

PARADISE RAILWAY
15in gauge

Paradise Park, Hayle, Cornwall TR27 4HY
Telephone: 01736 753365
Line length: 250yd, circular
OS Ref: SW555365
First opened: 1976
Operator: Paradise Park
Park entry fee

No	Name	Type	Builder	Built
3	Zebedee	4wDM	Lister	1938

A short line in a corner of this bird park with a tunnel, three level crossings and a station.

PIXIELAND MINIATURE RAILWAY
15in gauge

Pixieland Fun Park, West St, Kilkhampton, nr Bude, Cornwall EX23 9QW
Telephone: 01288 321225   *OS Ref:* SS250114   *Operator:* D. Vanstone
Line length: 200yd, circular   *First opened:* 1980   Park entry fee

No	Name	Type	Builder	Built
	Dennis	0-4-2T	Exmoor Steam Railway	1997
1	Pioneer	2-2wPM	K. Rosewell	1947

This line may seem short, but considering its location, cut into a steep hillside, it seems amazing that it was ever built in the first place. The little railway is an evergreen attraction among the children's rides at Pixieland, and has recently gained its own steam locomotive.

POOLE PARK RAILWAY
10¼in gauge

Poole Park, Parkstone Road, Poole, Dorset
Telephone (H): 01202 683701   *OS Ref:* SZ025912   *Operator:* B. Merrifield
Website: http://www.pprailway.freeserve.co.uk
Line length: 700yd, circular   *First opened:* 1949

No	Name	Type	Builder	Built
D107		4-6wPM	Southern Miniature Railways	c1958
D7000	Desmond	4-6wDH	Southern Miniature Railways	c1964

A long-established line meandering around the lake and through woodland in Poole Park.

RODE WOODLAND RAILWAY
7¼in gauge

Rode Bird Gardens, Rode, nr Bath, Somerset BA3 6QW
Telephone: 01373 830326   *OS Ref:* ST797546
Operators: D. Underhill and M. Marshall
Line length: 750yd, complex   *First opened:* 1988   Gardens entry fee

No	Name	Type	Builder	Built
	Yeoman Highlander	4w-4PM	Mardyke	c1981
	Sgt Murphy	0-6-0T	M. Marshall	1990
	Earl Haig	0-6-0T	M. Marshall/D. Underhill	1993

The 'Great Little Trains of Rode' wend their way from Woodland Central station through the trees and back again. A well-constructed line in a popular location. Special weekends with visiting locomotives are held during the year.

SMOKEY OAK RAILWAY
10¼in gauge

Woodland Park, Brokerswood, Westbury, Wiltshire BA13 4EH
Telephone: 01373 822238   *OS Ref:* ST838524   *Operator:* Woodland Park
Line length: 600yd, end to end   *First opened:* 1991   Park entry fee

On a sunny afternoon in spring 1999 Amelia *propels her train amongst the trees on the 10¼in gauge Smokey Oak Railway.* Simon Townsend

No	Name	Type	Builder	Built
	Amelia	4w-4wDH	Mardyke	1987

Woodland Park covers 80 acres of historic broad-leaved woodland, through part of which this line runs, taking passengers to Adventure Land station, for the adventure playground. All the structures are constructed from wood, including a substantial embankment and bridge.

TAMARISK MINIATURE RAILWAY 7¼in gauge

Old Macdonald's Farm, Porthcothan Bay, nr Padstow, Cornwall
Telephone: 01841 540829   *OS Ref:* SW861711
Line length: 200yd, circuit   *First opened:* 1989

No	Name	Type	Builder	Built
1680	Komotion	4w-2PH	D. Burwell	1986

There is one station, from where the train runs round a broadly square-shaped track.

WESTON MINIATURE RAILWAY 7¼in gauge

Beach Lawns, Marine Parade, Weston-super-Mare, North Somerset
Telephone: 01934 643510   *OS Ref:* ST316600   *Operator:* R. Bullock
Line length: 850yd, dumb-bell   *First opened:* 1981

No	Name	Type	Builder	Built
	Petra	2-4-0	G. White	1989
3	Dennis	4w-4PH	Bimpson/Bullock	1981
1	Dylan	S/O 4wPH	Greatrex/Bullock	1985

A popular line running round the putting green and then along the sea front at the southern end of Weston promenade.

WEYMOUTH BAY MINIATURE RAILWAY 10¼in gauge

Lodmoor Country Park, Weymouth, Dorset DT4 7SX
Telephone: 01305 785747   *OS Ref:* SY685807
Line length: 550yd, circular   *First opened:* 1983

No	Name	Type	Builder	Built
1890		S/O 2-6-0DH	Severn Lamb	1990

This line runs adjacent to some seaside amusements on the eastern outskirts of Weymouth. The station at Greenhill has two platforms, whilst the shed has three roads, accessed from a turntable.

AREA 2: SOUTH EAST

East Sussex, Hampshire, Kent, Surrey, West Sussex

BANKSIDE MINIATURE RAILWAY
8¼in gauge

Brambridge Park Garden Centre, Kiln Lane, Brambridge, Eastleigh, Hampshire SO50 6HT
Telephone: 01962 713707   *OS Ref:* SU467222   *Operator:* H. Merritt
Line length: 300yd, balloon   *First opened:* 1977

No	Name	Type	Builder	Built
815	Carolyn	2-6-2T		1924

Among public miniature railways this one is most unusual, featuring raised track of 8¼in gauge. The line first ran from end to end on a different site here. It moved to the present site in 1989 and was converted to a balloon loop in 1999. Upon its return the entire train is revolved using a 35ft diameter turntable. A fascinating location, not to be missed!

BENTLEY RAILWAY
5in/7¼in gauge

Bentley Wildfowl and Motor Museum, Halland, nr Uckfield, East Sussex BN8 5AF
Telephone: 01825 840573   *OS Ref:* TQ484159
Operator: Uckfield Model Railway Club
Website: http://www.geocities.com/Heartland/Plains/2143/index.html
Line length: 850yd, circular   *First opened:* 1985   Park entry fee

No	Name	Type	Builder	Built
	Hercules	0-4-0T		c1955
	Remus	0-4-0WT	P. Southern	1981
44804		4-6-0	Guest/Rogers	1984
1466		0-4-2T	W. Powell	1985
	Lorna	2-4-0	G. Billington	1991
70000	Britannia	4-6-2	W. Powell	1991
	William I	0-4-0ST	P. Southern	1991
	William II	0-4-0	P. Southern	1992
	Romulus	0-4-0	A. Lynn	1993
	Wren	0-4-0ST	W. Powell	1993
		0-4-0ST	D. Beeney	
4472	Flying Scotsman	4-6-2	S. Hills	
	Taurus	0-4-0T		
1310	Uckfield Flyer	4w-4wBER	Uckfield MRC	c1979
22	Blackhawk	4w-4wTG	P. Shott	1985
	Bulldog Spirit	0-4-0BE	Compass House	c1994
15324		0-6-0BE	Compass House	1995
		0-4-0BE	P. Southern	c1997
		0-4-0BE	G. Farmer	c1997

Quite a notable stud of locomotives is based at this model engineers' track. The line runs from Bentley Central station, and was considerably extended in 1995.

2-6-2T Carolyn *and her train at the outer terminus of the Bankside Miniature Railway. This photograph was taken on 10 October 1998, since when the railway has been extended so that trains no longer reverse here.* Simon Townsend

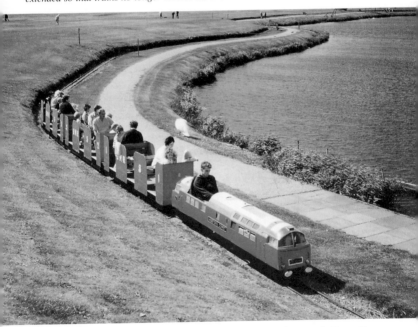

Western Comet *circumnavigates the lake at the Brooklands Miniature Railway, East Worthing.* Bruce Palmer

BROOKLANDS MINIATURE RAILWAY

10¼in gauge

Brooklands Pleasure Park, East Worthing, West Sussex
OS Ref: TQ173035 *Operator:* F. Rainson
Line length: 1,000yd, circular *First opened:* 1965

No	Name	Type	Builder	Built
	Western Comet	6-6wPH	Severn Lamb	1967

This line runs round the boating pool at Brooklands, between Worthing and Lancing. A steam loco ran here for a short time; quite extensive earthworks were necessary to get the track on to a level course.

CUCKOO HILL RAILWAY

7¼in gauge

Avon Valley Nurseries, South Gorley, nr Fordingbridge, Hampshire SP6 2PP
Telephone: 01425 653001 *OS Ref:* SU163105 *Operator:* R. Kinnison
Line length: 800yd, circular *First opened:* 1991

No	Name	Type	Builder	Built
	Jupiter	2-4-0	Moors Valley Railway	1991

This line was built by the team from the Moors Valley Railway, and is operated during the fruit-picking season. It runs through the fruit fields then returns via a tunnel. There is also a hand-worked 22in gauge line here, which crosses the 7¼in gauge circuit on the level — an unusual piece of trackwork.

EASTBOURNE MINIATURE STEAM RAILWAY PARK

7¼in gauge

Lottbridge Drove, Eastbourne, East Sussex BN23 6NS
Telephone: 01323 520229 *OS Ref:* TQ613012 *Operators:* M. and R. Wadey
Line length: 900yd, circular *First opened:* 1992 Park entry fee

No	Name	Type	Builder	Built
1	Thomas	0-4-2T	M. Wadey	1982
6172	Royal Green Jackets	4-6-0	M. Wadey	1988
3802		2-8-0	A. Newbery	1988
4039	Rachel	0-6-0	L. Markwick	1993
914	Eastbourne	4-4-0	L. Markwick	1999
D7042	Eastbourne Herald	4w-4wPE	M. Wadey	1987

Eastbourne's ⅛th scale miniature railway allows you to travel on replica coaches around Southbourne Lake; ideal for young and old alike. A railway-style café and lineside nature trail are available; regular special events (including 'Friends of Thomas the Tank Engine') are held.

EASTLEIGH LAKESIDE RAILWAY

10¼/7¼in gauge

Lakeside Country Park, Wide Lane, Eastleigh, Hampshire
Telephone: 023 8063 6612 *OS Ref:* SU446175
Operator: Eastleigh Lakeside Railway Ltd
Website: http://www.steamtrain.co.uk/
Line length: 2,000yd, dumb-bell *First opened:* 1992

2-6-2 Sir Arthur Heywood *at the Eastleigh Lakeside Railway on 3 October 1998.* Pat Henshaw

No	Name	Type	Builder	Built
1001	*The Monarch*	4-6-2	H. Bullock	1932
4789	*William Baker*	4-4-2	W. Baker	1947
3	*Francis Henry Lloyd*	4-8-4	Guest/Lloyd	1959
7	*Sandy River*	2-4-2	A. Bimpson	1983
10	*Sir Arthur Heywood*	2-6-2	K. Williamson	1984
6643		4-4wPH	R. Greatrex	1993
1994	*Eastleigh*	0-4-0+0-4-0DH	M. Millard	1994
1	*Florence*	S/O 0-6-0DH	ELR	2000
3221	*University of Southampton*	4w-4wBE	Southampton University	1999

Eastleigh Lakeside has recently joined the ranks of Britain's major miniature railways. A substantial new station building has been built at Eastleigh Parkway and a new platform added at Monks Brook Halt. The line is being converted to dual gauge (10¼in and 7¼ in) during early 2000 and a second track is also being added to allow continuous running. Periodic special events are held, including 'Days out with Thomas' weekends, for which No 1001 is authorised to appear as No 4 *Gordon*. *Sandy River* has been converted to oil firing and a new 2-6-2T is under construction.

FAVERSHAM MINIATURE RAILWAY   *9in gauge*

Faversham Garden Centre, London Road, Teynham, nr Faversham, Kent ME9 9JY
Telephone: 01795 521549   *OS Ref:* TQ970618   *Operator:* P. Reynolds
Line length: 350yd, end to end   *First opened:* 1995

No	Name	Type	Builder	Built
D7043		4w-4PM	Cromar White	c1974
(No 1)	*(Bertie)*	4-4wBE	T. Smith	1990
		4wPH	Iron Horse	1990

This line takes its unusual gauge from a private miniature railway not far away. Following a change in land ownership, the track is being relaid in a new direction to the back of the nursery.

GREAT COCKCROW RAILWAY   *7¼in gauge*

Hardwick Lane, Lyne, Chertsey, Surrey
Telephone: 01932 565474   *OS Ref:* TQ027662
Operator: Ian Allan Miniature Railway Supplies Ltd
Website: http://www.guess99.freeserve.co.uk/gcr.htm
Line length: 2,000yd, complex   *First opened:* 1964

No	Name	Type	Builder	Built
1239		4-4-0	Baldwin Bros	1912
1947	Eureka	4-6-2	L. Shaw	1926
2403	Lorna Doone	4-6-2	L. Shaw	1936
837		4-6-0	D. Curwen	1948
6100	Royal Scot	4-6-0	Barnett/Willoughby	1948
73755	Longmoor	2-10-0	J. Liversage	1948
7915	Mere Hall	4-6-0	Rowe	1952
206		2-6-0	D. Simmonds	1956
1935		2-6-0	H. Saunders	1975
1401		0-4-2T	R. Sills	1980
6100	Royal Scot	4-6-0	J. Butt	1981
5000	Sister Dora	4-6-0	A. Glaze	1981
8200		2-8-0	D. Pownall	c1983
70020	Mercury	4-6-2	N. Sleet	1985
4835		4-6-0	D. Benham	1985
850	Lord Nelson	4-6-0	D. Scarrott	1985
1249	Hecate	0-8-0	R. Sills	1986
6115	Scots Guardsman	4-6-0	P. Almond	1988
1442		4-4-2	Parkinson/Hammond	1988
5145		4-6-0	Axon/Sleet	1991
21C11	General Steam Navigation	4-6-2	Lester/Sleet	1993
8374		2-8-0	Glaze/Hancock	1993
34051	Sir Winston Churchill	4-6-2	N. Sleet	1995
70047	Lady of the Lake	4-6-2	J. Butt	1996
70054	Dornoch Firth	4-6-2	K. Richardson	1999
11		0-6-0PM	W. Jennings	1959
D7028	Alastair B. McLeod	4w-4wBE	A. Glaze	1982
40106		2-6w-6w-2PH	N. Sleet	1992

Steam raising in progress outside the locomotive shed at the Great Cockcrow Railway.
Robin Butterell

This is the inspirational home of 1½in (to the foot) scale railways in the UK. The above list represents a cross section of locomotives likely to be on shed, but it's always changing. Trains from Hardwick Central generally operate over either the circuit route through Everglades Junction (several times, in different directions) or climb the hill over a 45ft viaduct to terminate at Cockcrow Hill. Periodically a double-headed 'special' covers both routes; tickets may be booked in advance.

Most trains seat only 12 passengers but they run at very frequent intervals all afternoon. The intensive and highly professional operation is made possible only by strict block working between the three signalboxes. Authentic signalling is a particular feature, and the pace of events inside the boxes has to be seen to be believed.

The Great Cockcrow Railway is open on Sundays from May to October, from 2pm.

HOLLYCOMBE STEAM COLLECTION *7¼in gauge*

Iron Hill, Midhurst Road, Liphook, Hampshire GU30 7LP
Telephone: 01428 724900   *OS Ref:* SU852295
Operator: Hollycombe Steam & Woodland Garden Society
Website: http://www.hollycombe.co.uk/mainpage.htm
Line length: 400yd, circular   *First opened:* 1982   Park entry fee

No	Name	Type	Builder	Built
	(Bob)	0-4-2T	P. Howard	1981
	(Pauline)	0-4-0	Bennett Bros	1990
	(Dougal)	0-6-0PH		

This small miniature line is an ancillary attraction at the magnificent Hollycombe collection, where one can also ride upon 2ft and standard gauge lines, besides being entertained by the Bioscope and steam fairground rides.

LITTLEHAMPTON MINIATURE RAILWAY *12¼in gauge*

Mewsbrook Park, Littlehampton, West Sussex
OS Ref: TQ042016   *Operator:* C. Evans
Line length: 800yd, end to end   *First opened:* 1948

No	Name	Type	Builder	Built
(28588)	(Southern Belle)	S/O 4-4wDH	Fontwell/Duggin	1988

This long-established line runs from Norfolk Road, on the sea front, to Mewsbrook Park, a public park with boating rides, etc. For many years the railway was operated by two 4-6-4s built by John Thurston, who thought up the 12¼in gauge so as to give more stability than 10¼in.

MARWELL'S WONDERFUL RAILWAY *15in gauge*

Marwell Zoological Park, Colden Common, nr Winchester, Hampshire SO21 1JH
Telephone: 01962 777407   *OS Ref:* SU508216   *Operator:* Marwell Preservation Trust
Line length: 900yd, dumb-bell   *First opened:* 1987   Zoo entry fee

No	Name	Type	Builder	Built
	Princess Anne	S/O 2-6-0DH	Severn Lamb	1987

Marwell is world famous for its conservation and breeding of endangered species. The train ride gives close-up views of some of the animals. Trains run from Treetops Junction to Park End Halt, both stations being situated on balloon loops at either end of the line.

NEWHAVEN MINIATURE RAILWAY

7¼in gauge

Paradise Park, Avis Road, Newhaven, East Sussex BN9 0DH
Telephone: 01273 512123   *OS Ref:* TQ448023
Operator: Paradise Family Leisure Park
Line length: 200yd, circular   *First opened:* 1989

No	Name	Type	Builder	Built
D7068	Four Seasons	4w-4wDH	Mardyke	1989

A simple circuit at the back of this garden/leisure centre. The 'Hymek' hauls a set of Mardyke 'sit in' coaches finished in Brighton Belle colours.

PAULTONS PARK RIO GRANDE MINIATURE RAILWAY

15in gauge

Paultons Park, Ower, Romsey, Hampshire SO51 6AL
Telephone: 023 8081 4442   *OS Ref:* SU317167   *Operator:* Paultons Park Ltd
Line length: 700yd, circular   *First opened:* 1987   Park entry fee

No	Name	Type	Builder	Built
278		S/O 2-8-0DH	Severn Lamb	1986

This Severn Lamb train is just one of over 40 different attractions set in Paultons' gardens and parkland. Trains run clockwise from the station, alongside Paultons Lake for the last part of the journey.

RIVERVIEW MINIATURE RAILWAY

7¼in gauge

Riverview Garden Centre, Stopham Road, Pulborough, West Sussex RH20 1DS
Telephone: 01798 872981   *OS Ref:* TQ033183   *Operators:* A. and M. Jones
Line length: 900yd, complex   *First opened:* 1984

No	Name	Type	Builder	Built
	Hercules	0-4-0T	D. Underhill	1984
		0-6-0ST	S. Titley	c1987
		2-6-0	A. Jones	u/c
33008		4-4wPH	D. Titley	1995
		0-6-0BE	Compass House	1996

This line, at the back of the garden centre, has already had several layouts. It now features a two-road station, and was extended in 1999 so as to cross over itself and then run to a new picnic and adventure playground site. A spur leads to a turntable and then to steaming bays and a substantial shed.

ROMNEY, HYTHE & DYMCHURCH RAILWAY

15in gauge

New Romney, Kent TN28 8PL
Telephone: 01797 362353   *OS Ref (Hythe):* TR153347
Operator: The Romney, Hythe & Dymchurch Light Railway Co Ltd
Website: http://www.rhdr.demon.co.uk/rhdr.html
Line length: 14 miles, balloon   *First opened:* 1927

No	Name	Type	Builder	Built
1	Green Goddess	4-6-2	Davey Paxman	1925
2	Northern Chief	4-6-2	Davey Paxman	1925
3	Southern Maid	4-6-2	Davey Paxman	1926
4	The Bug	0-4-0	Krauss	1926
5	Hercules	4-8-2	Davey Paxman	1926
6	Samson	4-8-2	Davey Paxman	1926
7	Typhoon	4-6-2	Davey Paxman	1926
8	Hurricane	4-6-2	Davey Paxman	1926
9	Winston Churchill	4-6-2	Yorkshire Engine	1931
10	Doctor Syn	4-6-2	Yorkshire Engine	1931
11	Black Prince	4-6-2	Krupp	1937
4		4wDM	Motor Rail	1938
PW2		2w-2PM	RH&DR	1962
PW3	Redgauntlet	4wPM	Jacot/Keef	1977
12	John Southland	4w-4wDH	TMA Engineering	1983
14		4w-4wDH	TMA Engineering	1989

The RH&DR is probably the best-known miniature railway in the world. It is a complete railway system in miniature with comprehensive construction and maintenance facilities. There are six stations, 11 steam locomotives, two passenger diesels and three small i/c-powered engines for permanent way work. Passenger coaches (almost 70 in number) include a licensed 'Bar Car' which is the longest vehicle built to run on 15in gauge. The section between Hythe and New Romney is double-track.

No 2 Northern Chief *of the Romney, Hythe & Dymchurch Railway being maintained by its driver in a state of high polish before being put away for the night, 13 June 1994.* Simon Townsend

ROYAL VICTORIA RAILWAY

10¼in gauge

Royal Victoria Country Park, Netley, Southampton SO31 5GA
Telephone: 023 8045 6246   *OS Ref:* SU464079   *Operator:* P. Bowers
Line length: 1 mile, circular   *First opened:* 1996

No	Name	Type	Builder	Built
	Sir Walter Gower	4-4-2	Gower/Boughton	c1970
	Isambard Kingdom Brunel	2-6-0	D. Curwen	1977
	(Maurice the Major)	4w-4wDH	P. Bowers	1996
	(Claude the Colonel)	S/O 4w-4wDH	P. Bowers	2000

This new line uses part of the trackbed of an earlier 10¼in gauge railway, but is far more ambitious than its predecessor. A further steam locomotive is under construction, and planning permission has been granted for a terminus station, carriage shed/tunnel, and a further ½ mile of track. Definitely a line that deserves success, in this popular public park next to Southampton Water.

On 10 October 1998 2-6-0 Isambard Kingdom Brunel *makes another circuit of the Royal Victoria Railway.* Simon Townsend

STRAND MINIATURE RAILWAY   7¼in gauge

Strand Lido, Gillingham, Medway Towns (Kent)
Telephone: 01634 576744   *OS Ref:* TQ785694
Operator: Gillingham Borough Council
Line length: 400yd, circular   *First opened:* c1951

No	Name	Type	Builder	Built
253003	HMS Pembroke	4-4wPH	Mardyke	c1980
112		6w-6wDH	Mardyke	1987

A simple line from Apache station around the Lido, on the sea front at Gillingham. There is one station, a tunnel and a loop which is used only during two-train operation.

SWANLEY NEW BARN RAILWAY   7¼in gauge

New Barn Park, Swanley, Kent
Telephone: 01322 380956   *OS Ref:* TQ515696
Line length: 900yd, balloon   *First opened:* 1986

No	Name	Type	Builder	Built
		0-4-0	P. Beale	1988
	Lady Sarah	0-4-0T	J. Drury	1984
		0-4-0WT	L. Wood	1990
		2-6-2T	J. Stubbs	1992
414	Montezuma	2-8-0	J. Stubbs	1994
		4w-4BE	Pfeifferbahn	1986
D9015	Tulyar	6w-6wDH	Mardyke	1987
D7612	Steptoe	4w-4wPH	E. Ward	1988
D7076		4w-4wDH	Mardyke	1989
(47512)	County of Kent	6w-6wDH	Mardyke	1992
	Kestrel	6w-6wDH	Mardyke	1999
	Tegen	4wDH	Swanley	c1999

Trains depart from Lakeside station around an extended loop to New Barn, and return. This line features intricate signalling; its lever frame previously saw service on London Underground.

Steptoe in use at the Swanley New Barn Railway, on 30 May 1994. Alan Merrells

WELLINGTON COUNTRY PARK RAILWAY

7¼in gauge

Wellington Country Park, Riseley, nr Heckfield, Hampshire RG7 1SP
Telephone: 0118 932 6444 *OS Ref:* SU730627
Operator: Wellington Country Park
Line length: 500yd, circular *First opened:* 1980 Park entry fee

No	Name	Type	Builder	Built
	Charlotte	0-4-0+0-4-0DH	Crowhurst Engineering	1990

This line has been changed from a balloon loop to a circuit. Trains pass through a tunnel and over a pond on their way back to the station. There is a fair-sized shed accessed via a turntable.

WOKING GRANGE MINIATURE RAILWAY

6in and 7¼in gauge

Woking Homes Railcare Centre, Oriental Road, Woking, Surrey GU22 7BE
Telephone (H): 01703 440179   *OS Ref:* TQ014591
Operator: Woking Grange Miniature Railway
Line length: 250yd, end to end   *First opened:* 1960

No	Name	Type	Builder	Built
6in gauge:				
486		4-6-0	F. R. Hutchinson	1910
870	Frederick R. Hutchinson	4-6-2	F. R. Hutchinson	1925
	Canon Allen Edwards	4wBE	Barney/Millard	c1979
7¼in gauge:				
92203	Black Prince	2-10-0	D. Pownall	1979
	Wendy	0-4-0ST	M. Rickers	1980
45157		4-6-0		

A line in the grounds of Railcare Homes, running from Oriental Road to Jeffrey's Road station.

WOODLAND RAILWAY

10¼in gauge

Hotham Park, Bognor Regis, West Sussex PO21 1HW
OS Ref: SZ938995   *Operator:* J. Hudell
Line length: 900yd, circular   *First opened:* 1969

No	Name	Type	Builder	Built
	John Owen	4-4wPM	J. Hudell	1985

A circuit through woodland in Hotham Park, with the station next to a small amusement park.

A train on the Beale Railway (see right), headed by Sir Humphry Davy. *This photograph was taken in August 1995 when the 10¼in gauge line was relatively new.*
Bruce Whaley

28

BARKING RAILWAY

9½in gauge

Barking Park, Longbridge Road, Barking, Barking & Dagenham, Greater London
OS Ref: TQ446847
Line length: 350yd, end to end   First opened: 1954

No	Name	Type	Builder	Built
	Little Nan	4w-4wPE	Barking Corporation	1961

This line runs between Lodge and Lake stations, on virtually a straight alignment. The loco runs round its train at each end.

BEALE RAILWAY

10¼in gauge

Beale Park, Lower Basildon, Pangbourne, West Berkshire RG8 9NH
Telephone: 0118 984 5172   OS Ref: SU618782   Operator: J. Treble-Parker
Line length: 1,000yd, dumb-bell   First opened: 1989   Park entry fee

No	Name	Type	Builder	Built
	Sir Humphry Davy	4w-4wDH	G&SLE	1960

Between 1979 and 1994 a 7¼in gauge railway operated around this bird park. Now 10¼in gauge tracks have been laid, largely following the earlier line's alignment. Trains run from Howard's Halt, not far from the park entrance. An extension is planned here.

BLENHEIM PARK RAILWAY

15in gauge

Blenheim Palace, Woodstock, Oxfordshire OX20 1PX
Telephone: 01993 811091   OS Ref: SP443162   Operator: Blenheim Estate
Line length: 1,000yd, end to end   First opened: 1975   Park entry fee

No	Name	Type	Builder	Built
	Anna	4-6wDM	G&SLE	1960
	Sir Winston Churchill	S/O 0-6-2DH	Alan Keef	1992

This line performs a useful transport function, carrying visitors from the palace entrance down the hill to the garden centre. On peak days the train will be full as soon as the loco has run round, and then it will be off for its next trip.

EAST HERTS MINIATURE RAILWAY

7¼in gauge

Van Hage Garden Centre, Amwell Hill, Great Amwell, Hertfordshire SG12 9RP
Telephone: 01920 870811   OS Ref: TL367124
Operator: East Herts Miniature Railway Society
Line length: 600yd, complex   First opened: 1978

No	Name	Type	Builder	Built
	Dolbadarn	0-4-0ST	A. Robelou	c1983
	Romulus	0-4-0	C. Farmer	c1985
	T. C. B. Miller	0-4-2T	A. Robelou	1991
	Saint George	0-4-0	A. Cairns/ESSE	1991
	H. G. Harrison	0-4-0PM	B. Moretti	1977
	Hapi	2w-2-2wBE	P. Smith	c1987
	John A. Patten	2-6w-2PH	Barnard/Patten	1991
	Elf	2w-2-2wBE	P. Smith	1993

This line has two circuits, one inside the other, linked by a diamond crossover. The outer line includes a tunnel, whilst the inner one passes over a bridge.

FANCOTT LIGHT RAILWAY 7¼in gauge

Fancott Arms Public House, Fancott, nr Toddington, Bedfordshire LU5 6HT
Telephone: 01525 872366 *OS Ref:* TL022278 *Operator:* A. Wallman
Line length: 350yd, balloon *First opened:* 1996

No	Name	Type	Builder	Built
1		0-4-0	Dreadnought	1994
	Pippa	4wPH		

Trains run from the terminus at Fancott around a long balloon loop. The locomotive turns and runs round after the end of each journey.

GOLDING SPRING MINIATURE RAILWAY 5in/7¼in gauge

Buckinghamshire Railway Centre, Quainton Road Station, Station Road, Buckinghamshire HP22 4BY
Telephone: 01296 655450 *OS Ref:* SP741189
Operator: Vale of Aylesbury Model Engineering Society
Line length: 1,100yd, complex *First opened:* 1982 Site entry fee

No	Name	Type	Builder	Built
	Pipit	0-4-0ST	P. Booth	1992
	Bridget	0-4-2T	E. Goodchild	c1994
		0-6-0T	R. Urquhart	c1995
	Resolven	0-4-0ST	D. Minter	1996
3	John Pope	0-4-0T		
92220	Evening Star	2-10-0		
		4wBE	R. Tyler	1983
15103		0-6-0BE	M. Potter	1995
D7091		4w-4PM	D. Hill	

This line is located within the Buckinghamshire Railway Centre, adjacent to the standard gauge demonstration track in the 'up yard'. Trains run from Golding Spring Central station.

GREAT WOBURN RAILWAY 20in gauge

Woburn Safari Park, Woburn, Bedfordshire MK17 9QN
Telephone: 01525 290407 *OS Ref:* SP960340 *Operator:* Woburn Safari Park
Line length: 1,200yd, balloon *First opened:* 1994 Park entry fee

No	Name	Type	Builder	Built
	Robin Hood	S/O 4-6-4DH	Hudswell Clarke	1932
4472	Flying Scotsman	S/O 4-6-2DH	Hudswell Clarke	1933

This line runs from a terminus at Bison Halt, through a passing loop, to reach a sharply curved balloon loop, on the farthest side of which is Elephant Junction.

GULLIVERS RAILROAD
15in gauge

Gullivers Land, Livingstone Drive, Newlands, Milton Keynes, Buckinghamshire MK15 0DT
Telephone: 01908 609001   *OS Ref:* SP872399
Line length: 600yd, circular   *First opened:* 1999   Park entry fee

No	Name	Type	Builder	Built
		S/O 2-4-0+6wDE	Gullivers	1999

A 600yd circuit at this new children's theme park. Trains call at four stations: Main Street, Lilliput Land, Adventure Land, and Discovery Bay, where there is a stock siding.

HARROW & WEMBLEY MODEL ENGINEERS
3¼in/5in/7¼in gauge

Roxbourne Park, Field End Road, Eastcote, Harrow (Greater London)
OS Ref: TQ117868
Operator: Harrow & Wembley Society of Model Engineers
Line length: 660yd, complex

No	Name	Type	Builder	Built
	Tiny	0-4-0WT	M. Challans	c1980
1371		0-6-0PT		1981
5401	Sir Cumference	4-6-0	P. Beale	1982
	Peggy	0-4-0ST	C. Burgess	1982
5231		4-6-0	M. Challans	c1982
	Jenny	0-4-0ST	J. Cousins	c1984
1421		0-4-2T		c1990
	Hunslet	0-4-0ST	J. Cousins	1995
1104		0-4-0T		
		0-6-0PT		
26	Tally Ho	4wVBT	E. Basire	u/c
73XXX		4-6-0	J. Cousins	u/c
		0-6-0		2000
D3148		0-6-0BE	D. Jeavons	1997

This is quite an ingenious track, basically a circuit but with a chord line that can be gained from the terminus departure platform. Standard gauge prototypes prevail here. An extension to 930yd in length is under construction.

KNEBWORTH PARK MINIATURE RAILWAY
10¼in gauge

Knebworth House, Gardens and Park, nr Stevenage, Hertfordshire SG3 6PY
Telephone: 01438 812661   *OS Ref:* TL234215   *Operator:* S. Madgin
Line length: 700yd, dumb-bell   *First opened:* 1991

No	Name	Type	Builder	Built
	Exmoor Enterprise	6-6wPH	Curwen & Newbery	1965
	Uncle Jim	4-4wDM	J. Hughes	1968
	Meteor IV	2-4w-2DM	Shepperton Metal Products	1969
	Meteor V	2-4w-2PM	Shepperton Metal Products	1970
	Rhuddlan Castle	4w-4wDH	Fenlow	1972
	John Glenn	4wPM	Cocks/Fairweather	1994
	Fran	2-4w-2PM	B. Chapman	1998

This line runs through the grounds of Knebworth Park, adjacent to the car access to Knebworth House. The station is at the top of a short balloon loop, from where the line wends its way down before crossing to the opposite hillside. As with five of the locomotives, the coaches here also derive from Ian Allan's foray into miniature railway supplies.

MERTON MILL RAILWAY   10¼in gauge

Merton Abbey Mills, Watermill Way, Merton (Greater London) SW19
OS Ref: TQ265697   *Operator:* Little Giant Railways Ltd
Website: http://www.lgrailways.co.uk
Line length: 100yd, end to end   First opened: 1997

No	Name	Type	Builder	Built
	Trevithick	0-6-2T	R. Marsh	1975
	Lynton	2-4-4T	Narogauge/D. Yates	1984

Lynton has had a nomadic career, along with its rolling stock and sectional track making up the 'Narrower Gauge Railway'. Now owned by John Crosskey, a permanent line has been established at Merton Abbey Mills under the banner of 'Little Giant Railways'. Normally one of the engines can be found working the railway, whilst the other is kept a few miles away in the owner's workshops. The line runs beside the car park of Sainsbury's supermarket, from a station next to the River Wandle. The company is also hoping to run another, much longer, railway elsewhere in the locality.

PARADISE WILDLIFE PARK WOODLAND
RAILWAY   10¼in gauge

Paradise Wildlife Park, White Stubbs Lane, Broxbourne, Hertfordshire EN10 7QA
Telephone: 01992 468001   *OS Ref:* TL338068   *Operator:* Paradise Wildlife Park
Line length: 300yd, circular   *First opened:* 1981   Park entry fee

No	Name	Type	Builder	Built
		S/O 2-4w-2DM	Shepperton Metal Products	c1971

This 'sit in' steam outline loco hauls its two coaches around a circuit in part of the wildlife park. There is one station and a tunnel.

RUISLIP LIDO RAILWAY   12in gauge

Ruislip Lido, Reservoir Road, Ruislip, Hillingdon (Greater London) HA4 7TY
Telephone: 01895 622595   *OS Ref:* TQ089889
Operator: Ruislip Lido Railway Society Ltd
Line length: 1¼ miles, balloon
First opened: 1945

No	Name	Type	Builder	Built
	Mad Bess	2-4-0ST	Ruislip Lido Railway	1998
3	Robert	4w-4DH	Severn Lamb	1973
5	Lady of the Lakes	4w-4wDH	Ravenglass & Eskdale Rly	1985
7	Graham Alexander	4w-4wDH	Severn Lamb	1990

This line has improved beyond recognition since being taken over by volunteers in 1979. Trains now run from the original station at Woody Bay, through the loop at Eleanor's to Haste Hill, then over the new extension to Lakeside, not far from the Lido's main entrance. Movements are controlled by radio from the signalbox at Woody Bay. The steam locomotive is oil fired so as to avoid pyromania. Although run wholly by volunteers, the line is maintained and operated to the highest professional standards.

On 13 December 1998 Santa trains on the Ruislip Lido Railway were being hauled by Mad Bess. Trevor Rowe

SOUTHILL LIGHT RAILWAY

7¼in gauge

White Horse Public House, Southill, nr Biggleswade, Bedfordshire
Telephone: 01462 813364   *OS Ref:* TL148418
Line length: 400yd, circular   *First opened:* 1984

No	Name	Type	Builder	Built
	Herbie	4w-4PH	Severn Lamb	1984

An ingenious line running from Muchale Junction, with the circuit crossing over itself twice as well as underneath itself and through a tunnel.

VANSTONE WOODLAND RAILWAY
10¼in gauge

Vanstone Park Garden Centre, Hitchin Road, Codicote, nr Hitchin, Hertfordshire SG4 8TH
Telephone: 01438 820412   *OS Ref:* TL215201   *Operator:* S. Madgin
Line length: 550yd   *First opened:* 1986

No	Name	Type	Builder	Built
	Thomas	0-4-0ST	J. Brown	1986
	Lady Jane Gray	0-4-0ST	P. Gray	1996
	Sandham Castle	2-4w-2DM	Shepperton Metal Products	1969
	Meteor VI	2-4w-2DM	Shepperton Metal Products	1970
31423		4w-4PM	Ford	

The track here is basically a circuit, but with the station on a siding from which the train is propelled at the start of each run. The wooded section of the line includes some steep gradients.

WATFORD MINIATURE RAILWAY
10¼in gauge

Cassiobury Park, Watford, Hertfordshire
OS Ref: TQ090972   *Operator:* J. Price
Line length: 600yd, complex   *First opened:* 1959

No	Name	Type	Builder	Built
4179	Chiltern Shuttle	0-6-0	R. Morse	1946
7	Marri	2-6-0	Willis Engineering	1993
	Meteor II	2-4w-2DM	Shepperton Metal Products	1969
	Conway Castle	4w-4wDH	Fenlow	1972
	Nikki Louise	0-6-0DH	R. Prime	1988

This busy line has its station adjacent to the paddling pool/playground area in Cassiobury Park. Passengers ride over a gated crossing, and then round upon themselves in an area adjacent to the River Gade, a total journey of 1,020yd. *Marri* is a very powerful machine which was built in Australia and imported especially for use here; it has an unusual 'Briggs' firebox. At peak times operation here can be very slick indeed; other locos visit occasionally.

WILLEN MINIATURE RAILWAY
7¼in gauge

Willen Watersports Centre, Milton Keynes, Buckinghamshire
OS Ref: SP877397   *Operator:* F. Kenny
Line length: 800yd, balloon   *First opened:* 1989

No	Name	Type	Builder	Built
2	Ladybird	2-6-4T	F. Kenny	1992

A there-and-back line in a corner of this large public park, popular for its watersports facilities.

AREA 4: WEST MIDLANDS

Gloucestershire, Herefordshire, Warwickshire, West Midlands, Worcestershire.

COALYARD MINIATURE RAILWAY
7¼in gauge

Severn Valley Railway, Kidderminster Town Station, Comberton Hill, Kidderminster, Worcestershire DY10 1QX
Telephone: 01562 744667 *OS Ref:* SO837762 *Operator:* Coalyard MR Group
Line length: 450yd, end to end *First opened:* 1988

No	Name	Type	Builder	Built
	Percy	0-4-0WT	K. Wilson	1994
	Allan A.	0-4-0ST	K. Wilson	1999
6	Great Western	4wBE	Shaw/Maxitrak	1988
	Louis Shaw	4w-2PH	B. and R. Shaw	1990
	Petrel	0-4-0+0-4-0BE	P. Gardner	1991
		S/O 4wPH	R. Dawson	1992
	Nicky	0-4-0PH	Roanoke	1998
7000		4w-4PH	D. Renner	

This line runs from a terminus in front of Kidderminster Railway Museum, out and back parallel to the Severn Valley Railway platforms. All funds raised go towards improving the miniature railway or are donated to restoration projects on the SVR. The railway normally operates on Saturdays from March to December, and to coincide with the SVR's special events. The loco sheds are at the far end of the line.

DRAYTON MANOR PARK MINIATURE RAILWAYS
10¼in gauge

Drayton Manor Family Fun Park, Tamworth, Staffordshire B79 8HH
Telephone: 01827 287979 *OS Ref:* SK194016 *Operators:* The Bryan family
Website: http://www.draytonmanor.co.uk/
Line lengths: 850yd, circular; 450yd, end to end *First opened:* 1951
Park entry fee

No	Name	Type	Builder	Built
No 1		S/O 2-8-0PH	Severn Lamb	1971
7, 278		S/O 2-8-0DH	Severn Lamb	1983

It was Mr G. Bryan, chairman of Drayton Manor, who first ordered the now ubiquitous 'Rio Grande' 2-8-0 from Severn Lamb, along with the distinctive canopied coaches which seat two side by side. They still run this original locomotive, along with a second 'Rio' which operates on a separate track.

ECKINGTON NARROW GAUGE RAILWAY
7¼in gauge

Beacons Nurseries, Tewkesbury Road, Eckington, Pershore, Worcestershire WR10 3DG
Telephone: 01386 750359 *OS Ref:* SO924411 *Operator:* R. Washington
Line length: 650yd, balloon loop *First opened:* 1996

No	Name	Type	Builder	Built
No 4	Triumph	4wPM	M. Tebbett	1984
	Tiny Tim	0-4-0PH	R. Washington	1993
	Deudraeth Castle	0-6-0PH	R. and L. Washington	1995

This railway is being extended, and is anticipated to be a balloon loop run by the 2000 season, adjacent to the nursery here. *Deudraeth Castle* is a model of *Harlech Castle* on the Ffestiniog Railway; it is unusual on 7¼in gauge in being both a model and enabling the driver to sit inside the cab. The line opens to the public only on Saturdays, from 2pm.

The Eckington Narrow Gauge Railway features this attractive terminus.
Robin Butterell

FINNEY GARDENS RAILWAY

7¼in gauge

Finney Gardens, Bucknall Park, Stoke-on-Trent, Staffordshire
OS Ref: SJ900476
Line length: 1,000yd, circular

Operator: Stoke-on-Trent Model Engineers Ltd
First opened: 1996

No	Name	Type	Builder	Built
407	Old Rube	2-8-0	Milner Engineering	1983
1	Biddy	0-4-0T	M. Williams	1985
	Lady Be	0-4-0ST	D. J. Bussey	1988
3	Jill	0-4-0ST	R. Gray	1993
6	Waldenburg	0-6-0T	R. Hammond	1997
		4w-4wDH	Stoke-on-Trent MES	1996
		4w-4w+4-4BE	Express Locos	2000

This line features a substantial enclosed station, and two parallel steel bridges over the River Trent. The complete circuit, including a new section around the children's zoo, was opened in August 1999. The new section features a level crossing with gates activated by infra-red sensors.

36

A well-loaded train departs from the station at the Finney Gardens Railway on 31 August 1998. Trevor Rowe

Mike Rees's GWR Museum in Coleford is a jolly location with quite a variety of exhibits. Among the attractions is this short 7¼in gauge line, seen in operation on 22 August 1998. Simon Townsend

GWR MUSEUM MINIATURE RAILWAY

7¼in gauge

GWR Museum, Old Goods Shed, Coleford, Gloucestershire
Telephone: 01594 833569   *OS Ref:* SO574107   *Operator:* M. Rees
Line length: 100yd, circular   *First opened:* 1988

No	Name	Type	Builder	Built
2091	Victor	0-4-0ST	K. Hardy	c1984
	Little John	4-4wBER	T. Smith	1979
		4wBE	M. Rees/Maxitrak	c1989

A circular line running around this museum, in the old goods shed at Coleford. Further locomotives are on display inside the building, and a 'Romulus' is under construction.

HILCOTE VALLEY RAILWAY

7¼in gauge

Fletchers Garden & Leisure Centre, Bridge Farm, Stone Road, Eccleshall, Staffordshire ST21 6JY
Telephone (H): 01785 284553   *OS Ref:* SJ842292   *Operator:* R. Greatrex
Website: http://www.hilcote.co.uk/welcome.htm
Line length: 500yd, circular   *First opened:* 1993

No	Name	Type	Builder	Built
	Lady Madcap	0-4-0ST	K. Massey	1991
	Kashmir	0-6-0T	M. Marshall/D. Underhill	1993
	Primrose	0-4-2T	D. Halstead	1997
6141	The North Staffordshire Regiment	4-6-0	R. Greatrex	1998
		0-6-0PH	R. Greatrex	2000

Roger Greatrex is now a full-time builder of miniature railway equipment and this line is a good showcase for his abilities. The railway runs around the play area, then out behind the garden centre and round a small lake.

LEASOWES MINIATURE RAILWAY

7¼in gauge

Leasowes Park, Mucklow Hill, Halesowen, Dudley, West Midlands
Telephone: 01562 710614   *OS Ref:* SO976840   *Operator:* M. Male
Line length: 250yd, end to end   *First opened:* 1990

No	Name	Type	Builder	Built
46210	Prince Edward	2-6-2	J. and W. Gower	1936
50021	William Shenstone	4-4wPM	M. Male	1991

The line runs along a canal towpath with views overlooking the lake and park, which is grade one listed. The railway operates on Sundays all year round, from 2pm.

LEISURERAIL STEAM RAILWAY

7¼in gauge

Hollybush Garden Centre, Warstone Road, Shareshill, Wolverhampton WV10 7LX
Telephone: 01922 418050   *OS Ref:* SJ966064   *Operator:* Leisurerail Ltd
Line length: 950yd, circular   *First opened:* 1996

At Hollybush Central station on the Leisurerail Steam Railway, passengers have joined the next train, which will be headed by No 3, 19 September 1998.
Simon Townsend

No	Name	Type	Builder	Built
	Samuel Whitbread	0-4-2	Roberts/Forshaw	1986
	Malandra	0-4-2	TMA Engineering	1987
3		4w-4wPH	E. Smith	1987
645		4-4wPH	R. Greatrex	1998

This immaculately laid circuit runs around two small lakes, and features a tunnel and a bridge over a stream. There is a steeply graded spur from the station up to the shed area.

MALVERN HILLS NARROW GAUGE RAILWAY — 7¼in gauge

Malvern Hills Children's Zoo, Solitaire, Danemore Cross, Welland, Worcestershire WR13 6NJ
Telephone: 01684 310016
Line length: 400yd, circular
OS Ref: SO802410
First opened: 1986   Zoo entry fee

No	Name	Type	Builder	Built
3039		4-4wPM	D. Curwen	1970

A simple line running from a station through the paddocks of this small zoo.

THE NICKELODEON LINE

Ashorne Hall Nickelodeon, Ashorne Hill, nr Warwick, Warwickshire CV33 9QN
Telephone: 01926 651444   *OS Ref:* SP314587   *Operator:* G. Whitehead
Line length: 700yd, balloon   *First opened:* 1994   Gardens entry fee

No	Name	Type	Builder	Built
	Ashorne	2-4-2T	Exmoor Steam Railway	1994
	Bella	2-4-2PH	Exmoor S R/P Camps	1994

Ashorne Hall houses the Nickelodeon collection of mechanical music, along with a 'Mighty Cinema Organ' upon which there are performances on most opening days at 4pm. In the grounds of the hall the Nickelodeon Line runs from Orange Blossom Halt around and up, through the tunnel, round the loop and back; trains call at New Lodge station on the return journey. Notwithstanding the minimum gauge of this line (made necessary by its curves and grades), its constructors have paid particular attention to detail; notice the ornate coaches, picturesque stations and stock shed.

PERRYGROVE RAILWAY

Perrygrove Farm, Coleford, Gloucestershire GL16 8QB
Telephone: 01594 834991   *OS Ref:* SO579095   *Operator:* Treasure Train Ltd
Line length: 1,200yd, end to end   *First opened:* 1996   Site entry fee

No	Name	Type	Builder	Built
	Spirit of Adventure	0-6-0T	Exmoor Steam Railway	1993
	Ursula	0-6-0T	J. Waterfield	1999
No 2	Workhorse	4wDM	Motor Rail	1967

Situated just to the south of Coleford, Michael Crofts' railway is based firmly on the minimum gauge principles first promoted by Sir Arthur Heywood 100 years ago. The line takes the form of a squashed 'S'; trains double back upon themselves at a higher level, before sweeping round and climbing the grade to Oakiron. Children can follow the clues to be rewarded with discoveries of treasure. *Ursula* is a replica of one of Sir Arthur Heywood's locomotives built for the Eaton Hall Railway; it is based here but may visit other railways occasionally.

RUDYARD LAKE RAILWAY

Rudyard Old Station, Rudyard, Leek, Staffordshire ST13 8PF
Telephone (H): 01260 272862   *OS Ref:* SJ956579   *Operator:* P. Hanton
Line length: 1½ miles, end to end   *First opened:* 1978

No	Name	Type	Builder	Built
5013	Ivanhoe	4-4-0	H. Bullock	1937
5	Rudyard Lady	4-4wDM	L. Smith	1989
1	Kingsley	0-4-0DM	Curwen & Newbery	1954
2		4wPM	T. Stanhope	1969
6	River Churnet	2-4-2T	Exmoor Steam Railway	1993

This line runs along a wooded standard gauge trackbed from the car park to The Dam, Lakeside and Hunthouse Wood, a very attractive setting for a miniature railway. A steam boat gives rides on the lake nearby.

At the Perrygrove Railway on 31 October 1999, James Waterfield and Sir Peter Heywood are seen on the footplate of Ursula, *whilst the preceding train has been brought in by* Spirit of Adventure. Simon Townsend

A train at Hunthouse Wood terminus on the Rudyard Lake Railway, ready to return alongside the lake behind River Churnet. Peter Hanton

SAFARI EXPRESS

15in gauge

West Midland Safari & Leisure Park, Spring Grove, Bewdley,
Worcestershire DY12 1LF
Telephone: 01299 402114   *OS Ref:* SO804756
Operator: W. M. Leisure & Safari Park
Line length: 700yd, end to end   *First opened:* 1979   Park entry fee

No	Name	Type	Builder	Built
278		S/O 2-8-0DH	Severn Lamb	1979

This Severn Lamb train ferries visitors from a station near the park entrance round to the 'leisure area' where many other amusement rides can be found.

WESTON PARK RAILWAY

7¼in gauge

Weston Park, Weston-under-Lizard, nr Shifnal, Staffordshire TF11 8LE
Telephone: 01952 850207   *OS Ref:* SJ808106   *Operator:* B. Whaley
Website: http://www.weston-park.com/
Line length: 1,200yd, dumb-bell   *First opened:* 1980   Park entry fee

No	Name	Type	Builder	Built
		4w-4wDH	B. Whaley/R. Greatrex	2000
5901	Mount Kenya 17058ft	4-8-2+2-8-4	Milner Engineering	1977

One of the longest and best maintained 7¼in lines, trains run from the bottom station near the house, up the long hill and on to single track, through the passing loop and then to the top balloon loop among some trees. On the return journey trains call at the adventure playground station, before rolling down over a long viaduct to the bottom station again. The railway runs through an outstanding collection of mature trees on the Weston Park Estate. There is a large shed which can house visiting locomotives, some of which may appear during the operating season. *Mount Kenya 17058ft* is owned by the National Railway Museum and will be on loan here during 2000.

AREA 5: EAST MIDLANDS

Derbyshire, Leicestershire, Nottinghamshire.

AMERICAN ADVENTURE RAILROAD   15in gauge

American Adventure, Shipley, nr Ilkeston, Derbyshire DE7 5SX
Telephone: 01773 531521   *OS Ref:* SK443444   *Operator:* American Adventure
Website: http://www.adventureworld.co.uk/homepage.html
Line length: 1 mile, circular   *First opened:* 1985   Park entry fee

No	Name	Type	Builder	Built
		S/O 2-6-0DH	Severn Lamb	1986
		S/O 2-6-0DH	Severn Lamb	1988

Trains run clockwise around a lake, pausing en route at five different halts.

HALL LEYS MINIATURE RAILWAY   9½in gauge

Hall Leys Park, Matlock, Derbyshire
OS Ref: SK300600   *Operator:* Miniature Railway Co Ltd
Line length: 200yd, end to end   *First opened:* 1948

No	Name	Type	Builder	Built
	Little David	6wDH	Allcock/Coleby Simkins	1974

A simple line running up and down the side of Hall Leys Park.

MANOR PARK MINIATURE RALWAY   7¼in gauge

Manor Park Road, Glossop, Derbyshire
OS Ref: SE041947   *Operator:* A. Sowden
Line length: 500yd, balloon   *First opened:* 1970

No	Name	Type	Builder	Built
	Percy	0-4-0T	P. Land	1988
	Galahad	4w-4wBE	Cromar White	1970
7	Jerry	S/O 4w-2PM	R. Kay	1983
No 1	Sir Ian	S/O 0-4-0PM	J. Pinder	1984
	High Peak	4-4wPH	A. Bimpson	1992
	Manor	4wPH	Pfeifferbahn	1993

The station here has a run-round loop, and the balloon loop can be used as a circuit. There
are spurs off the balloon loop to the carriage and loco sheds.

---

*Left: Fares are collected at the Manor Park Miniature Railway, Glossop, on 16 May
1999. The locomotive is based on a Class 91 electric prototype, whilst its 7¼in gauge
rails have been made from point rodding.* Dave Holroyde

The next train at the Markeaton Park Light Railway will be hauled by 0-4-2T Markeaton Lady on 5 April 1998. Dave Holroyde

MARKEATON PARK LIGHT RAILWAY

15in gauge

Markeaton Park, Derby, Derbyshire
Telephone (H): 01623 552292   *OS Ref:* SK335372   *Operators:* J. and J. Bull
Website: http://freespace.virgin.net/david.lowe1/markeatonplr.htm
Line length: 1,400yd, end to end   *First opened:* 1989

No	Name	Type	Builder	Built
	Markeaton Lady	0-4-2T	Exmoor Steam Railway	1996
No 6		4wDM	Lister	1952
	Cromwell	4wDH	Ruston & Hornsby	1960
D5905		4w-4wDH	J. Brown	1995

This railway has been greatly extended and improved since it was taken over by by John and Jane Bull in 1996. Trains now run from the main car park (entrance from the A38 Derby ring road) through the park and over two major bridges to a second terminus adjacent to the play area at Mundy Halt. Most services are worked by *Markeaton Lady,* along with three luxurious enclosed coaches, also built by Exmoor Steam Railway.

MELTON MOWBRAY MINIATURE RAILWAY

10¼in gauge

Egerton Park Sportsground, Leicester Road, Melton Mowbray, Leicestershire
Telephone: 01664 566313   *OS Ref:* SK750190
Operator: Melton Mowbray Town Estate
Line length: 500yd, circular   *First opened:* 1975

No	Name	Type	Builder	Built
D1417		2w-2PM	G. Wilcox	1968

A simple line running around the bowling green and play area, next to the River Eye.

NOTTINGHAM MODEL ENGINEERS
7¼in gauge

Nottingham Transport Heritage Centre, Ruddington, Nottinghamshire
Telephone: 0115 940 5705   *OS Ref:* SK574322
Operator: Nottingham Society of Model & Experimental Engineers Ltd
Line length: 800yd, circular   *First opened:* 1998   Site entry fee

No	Name	Type	Builder	Built
4472	*Flying Scotsman*	4-6-2	W. Kirkland	1947
60532	*Blue Peter*	4-6-2	W. Kirkland	1951
	Hilde	0-6-2T	J. Hawker	c1972
	Jean/Mary	0-4-0	R. Morgan	c1987
498		0-6-0T	L. Reed	1988
30926	*Repton*	4-4-0	G. Starbuck	1995
D60	*Lytham St Annes*	2-6w-6w-2BE	Maxitrak	1996
	R. E. Whomsley	4w-4wPH	R. Whomsley	1999

This new track lies within the grounds of the Great Central (Northern) site at Ruddington. Trains run from Little Ruddington station through a tunnel, along behind the small gauge elevated line, and then either way around a reversible loop accessed via a diamond crossing.

PAVILION GARDENS MINIATURE RAILWAY
12¼in gauge

Pavilion Gardens, St Johns Road, Buxton, Derbyshire SK17 6XN
Telephone: 01298 23114   *OS Ref:* SK055734
Operator: High Peak Borough Council
Line length: 300yd, circular   *First opened:* 1972

No	Name	Type	Builder	Built
		S/O 0-6-0DH	A. Keef	2000

A circuit through the park, crossing two bridges over a stream. The line was formerly 10¼in gauge, and was rebuilt using 12¼in gauge track during winter 1999/2000.

QUEENS PARK MINIATURE RAILWAY
10¼in gauge

Queens Park, Boythorpe Road, Chesterfield, Derbyshire
Telephone: 01246 345555   *OS Ref:* SK378709
Operator: Chesterfield Borough Council
Line length: 550yd, circular   *First opened:* 1976

No	Name	Type	Builder	Built
		S/O 2-6-0DH	Severn Lamb	1988

A train of Severn Lamb stock running around the lake in this public park. One trip is two circuits.

TWYCROSS ZOO MINIATURE RAILWAY *10¼in gauge*

Twycross Zoo, Twycross, nr Atherstone, Leicestershire CV9 3PX
Telephone: 01827 880250 *OS Ref:* SK320061 *Operator:* Twycross Zoo
Line length: 650yd, circular *First opened:* 1969 Zoo entry fee

No	Name	Type	Builder	Built
7, 278		S/O 2-8-0PH	Severn Lamb	1983

The line here includes a spiral section over which trains descend just after leaving the station. The locomotive was one of a number built carrying numbers 7 on the chimney and 278 on the cab side.

WHITEPOST WONDERLAND RAILWAY *7¼in gauge*

Wonderland Pleasure Park, White Post Corner, Farnsfield, Nottinghamshire NG22 8XH
Telephone: 01623 882773 *OS Ref:* SK627572 *Operator:* D. Pepper
Line length: 400yd, balloon *First opened:* 1996 Park entry fee

No	Name	Type	Builder	Built
		2-6wDH	Tucktonia	1986
2	Mickey	S/O 4w-2PH	R. Greatrex	1999

The new locomotive here is petrol powered, but features the synchronised sound of a steam locomotive!

Trains at the Whitepost Wonderland Railway reverse by unusual means, the locomotive being parked on the stub of track shown here on 3 May 1999, whilst the train is hand shunted over the turntable into the departure platform behind.
R. N. Jones

AREA 6: EASTERN COUNTIES

Cambridgeshire, Essex, Lincolnshire, Norfolk,
North East Lincolnshire, North Lincolnshire, Suffork.

AUDLEY END MINIATURE RAILWAY
10¼in gauge

Audley End House, Saffron Walden, Essex
Telephone: 01799 541354   *OS Ref:* TL523378   *Operator:* Lord Braybrooke
Line length: 1 mile, dumb-bell   *First opened:* 1964

No	Name	Type	Builder	Built
3548	Lord Braybrooke	2-6-2	D. Curwen	1948
4433		4-4-2	Curwen & Newbery	1965
489	Sara Lucy	2-8-2	D. Curwen	1977
691	Henrietta Jane	0-4-0+0-4-0PH	A. Crowhurst	1991
24		2-6-2	D. Curwen	1991
1680	Loyalty	4-4-0	D. Curwen	1994
	Barbara Curwen	2-4-2	D. Curwen	1997
D1011	Western Thunderer	6-6wPM	Curwen & Newbery	1964
682	Doris	0-6-0PM	D. Curwen	1982

A racetrack of a line with an impressive array of locomotives on shed, from a Great
Northern Atlantic to an enormous Denver & Rio Grande 2-8-2. Audley End station has its
own car park not far from the entrance drive to the house. After passing the shed area,
trains bowl along a long straight, then cross the River Fulfen and River Cam. They then
enter a very long and curvaceous balloon loop through the woods, passing Forest Deep
Halt, and through a long tunnel. The loop points are centre sprung, so alternate trains take
this section in opposite directions before returning from whence they came. Watch out for
the teddies that live in the woods.

The Audley End Miniature Railway, with trains in the station headed by No 24 and
Doris. Robin Butterell

BARLEYLANDS MINIATURE STEAM RAILWAY

7¼in gauge

Barleylands Visitor Centre, Barleylands Road, Billericay, Essex CM11 2UD
Telephone: 01268 532253   *OS Ref:* TQ695920
Operator: H. R. Philpot and Son (Barleylands) Ltd
Line length: 800yd, end to end   *First opened:* 1989   Park entry fee

No	Name	Type	Builder	Built
	Maid of Benfleet	4-4-2T	J. Clarke	1970
	Vulcan	2-6-0	J. Clarke	1972
92203	Black Prince	2-10-0	J. Clarke	1981
70000	Britannia	4-6-2	J. Clarke	1981
	(Gowrie)	0-6-4T	H. Dyson	1990

From the shed area behind the museum, this line drops down in a C shape to a run-round loop at Littlewood Junction. From there a further line runs, more or less straight, to Boot Fair station. Because of its layout the railway is usually operated in two halves. Most of the equipment here came from a notable private railway at Benfleet, alas now closed.

BASILDON MINIATURE RAILWAY

10¼in gauge

Wat Tyler Country Park, Pitsea, Essex
Telephone: 01268 550088   *OS Ref:* TQ738865   *Operator:* D. Bundock
Line length: 1,200yd, balloon   *First opened:* 1988

No	Name	Type	Builder	Built
	Western Courier	6-6wPH	Severn Lamb	1969

A line running through this extensive country park, from the boat museum to the marina.

BELTON HOUSE MINIATURE RAILWAY

7¼in gauge

Belton House Park & Gardens, Belton, nr Grantham, Lincolnshire NG32 2LS
Telephone: 01476 566116   *OS Ref:* SK927394   *Operator:* The National Trust
Line length: 500yd, end to end   *First opened:* 1979   Grounds entry fee

No	Name	Type	Builder	Built
		4w-4PH	G. Johnson	1979
		4w-4wDH	Mardyke	1998

A simple line running out-and-back through woodlands on the estate of Belton House.

BRESSINGHAM STEAM MUSEUM AND GARDENS

15in and 10¼in gauge

Diss, Norfolk IP22 2AB
Telephone: 01379 687386   *OS Ref:* TM080805
Operator: Bressingham Steam Preservation Co Ltd
Website: http://www.bressingham.co.uk/Home.htm   Site entry fee
Waveney Valley Railway; 15in gauge   1½ miles, circular   *First opened:* 1973
Garden Railway; 10¼in gauge   700yd, balloon   *First opened:* 1995

No	Name	Type	Builder	Built
15in gauge:				
1662	*Rosenkavalier*	4-6-2	Krupp	1937
1663	*Mannertreu*	4-6-2	Krupp	1937
	Ivor	4wDH	Frenze Engineering	1979
10¼in gauge:				
No 1	*Alan Bloom*	0-4-0ST	P. Gray	1995

These miniature lines form two of the attractions at Bressingham Steam Museum. Trains on the Waveney Valley Railway are timed to coincide with those on the 2ft gauge Nursery Line, which crosses over it, so that passengers can see the other train at work. The Garden Railway is an enlarged version of a 9½in gauge line which dated back to Bressingham's first public opening. Steam days are Sundays, Thursdays and peak Wednesdays. A 12in gauge 4-4-0T is on display in the museum here, whilst a 15in gauge 4-6-2 *Flying Scotsman* is being overhauled for possible use on the Waveney Valley Railway.

The Garden Railway at Bressingham Steam Museum is an example of 10¼in gauge pushed to its widest, highest and heaviest dimensions. 0-4-0ST Alan Bloom *is seen from the train on 26 May 1999.*
Simon Townsend

Bure Valley Railway No 8, about to set off with its train from the impressive station at Aylsham, 14 May 1998.
Simon Townsend

BURE VALLEY RAILWAY

Aylsham, Norfolk NR11 6BW
Telephone: 01263 733858   *OS Ref:* TG196264
Operator: Bure Valley Railway (1991) Ltd
Website: http://bvrw.co.uk
Line length: 8¾ miles, end to end   First opened: 1990

No	Name	Type	Builder	Built
1	*Wroxham Broad*	2-6-4T	G&SLE	1964
6	*Blickling Hall*	2-6-2	Winson Engineering	1994
7	*Spitfire*	2-6-2	Winson Engineering	1994
8	*(Thunder)*	2-6-2T	BVR/Winson	1998
10	*Mark Timothy*	2-6-4T	Winson Engineering	1999
11		2-8-0	T. Turner/BVR	u/c
4	*The Apprentice*	4wDH	Hunslet	1954
7		S/O 4wDM	Lister Blackstone	1960
3	*2ⁿᵈ Air Division USAAF*	4w-4wDH	J. Edwards	1989

Trains run from Aylsham through Brampton, Buxton and Coltishall to Wroxham; most of the formation is on a standard gauge trackbed. The 'ZB' class 2-6-2s are among the largest and most powerful 15in gauge locomotives ever built. The components have been adapted to tank engine form to create Nos 8 and 10. No 8 is based on a Vale of Rheidol prototype and is oil fired, whilst 10 is based on a locomotive from the erstwhile County Donegal system in Ireland. Special events include popular 'Days out with Thomas' and Santa trains; the railway also offers driving courses.

CLEETHORPES COAST LIGHT RAILWAY

Lakeside Station, Kings Road, Cleethorpes, North East Lincolnshire DN35 0AG
Telephone: 01472 604657   *OS Ref:* TA315078
Operator: Cleethorpes Coast Light Railway Ltd
Line length: 1,200yd, end to end   First opened: 1971

A low season train at the Cleethorpes Coast Light Railway on 24 May 1999 was being worked by their 4wDM tram engine, seen at Kingsway station. Simon Townsend

No	Name	Type	Builder	Built
	Katie	2-4-2	G&SLE	1956
	The Flower of the Forest	4wVBT	R&ER Co	1985
No 24		2-6-2	Fairbourne	1990
		4wDM	Lister	1944
	John	4-4wDH	Minirail	1954
		S/O 2-8-0DH	Severn Lamb	1972
		2w-2PM	A. Moss	1992

This is the latest of six different miniature railways to have operated in Cleethorpes over the years, having recently been regauged from 14½in gauge. Trains run from Lakeside Station up the hill past the shed area, then alongside the sea wall to Kingsway. For many years two Severn Lamb 'Rio's were the sole motive power, but the railway now has a good volunteer support group and trains are regularly steam hauled. The line was realigned with a new 40yd viaduct at the Kingsway end in early 2000.

FELIXSTOWE MINIATURE RAILWAY   7¼in gauge

Sea Road, Felixstowe, Suffolk
OS Ref: TM298339   *Operator:* Ocean Amusements
Line length: 150yd, circular   *First opened:* 1960

No	Name	Type	Builder	Built
		4w-4PM	Cromar White	1971
350024		4-4wPH	Mardyke	c1983

A small circle of track among the attractions on the promenade at Felixstowe.

FERRY MEADOWS MINIATURE RAILWAY   10¼in gauge

Nene Park, Oundle Road, Peterborough, Cambridgeshire
Telephone: 01205 364352   *OS Ref:* TL148975   *Operator:* Cubedart Ltd
Line length: 700yd, end to end   *First opened:* 1979

No	Name	Type	Builder	Built
1950	Henry	4-6-2	E. Dove	1950
	Ivor	0-4-0ST	Jones/Mills	1993
	Charles	S/O 0-6-0DH	A. Keef	1999

A popular line located in a large public park, a short walk from Ferry Meadows station on the Nene Valley Railway. The track descends from Ham Lane to Gunwade Lane; the loco is turned and runs round its train at each end. A 10¼in gauge Darjeeling & Himalayan Railway 0-4-0ST is under construction, which is expected to run here in due course.

FRITTON LAKE MINIATURE RAILWAY   10¼in gauge

Fritton Lake Countryworld, Fritton, nr Great Yarmouth, Norfolk NR31 9HA
Telephone: 01493 488208   *OS Ref:* TM477001
Line length: 600yd, balloon   *First opened:* 1996   Park entry fee

No	Name	Type	Builder	Built
	(Derek)	4wDM	Shepperton Metal Products	1968
	Nevada	4-4wPH	A. Bimpson	1996
		4wDH	G. Fairweather	1998

Fritton Lake is a picturesque country park with numerous facilities for the whole family. The railway runs through woodland and offers views across the two-mile-long lake.

GRIMSBY & CLEETHORPES MODEL ENGINEERS

5in/7¼in gauge

Waltham Windmill, Brigsley Road, Waltham, nr Grimsby, North East Lincolnshire DN37 0JZ
OS Ref: TA259034 *Operator:* Grimsby & Cleethorpes Model Engineering Society
Line length: 400yd, circular

No	Name	Type	Builder	Built
		0-4-2T	G. Dobbs	c1978
1366		0-6-0PT	D. Smith	1990
32670		0-6-0T	J. Britton	1994
2	Kimberley	0-4-0T	P. Collins	1995
84008		2-6-2T	J. Britton	1998
3	Thomas Jack	0-4-0ST	P. Clark	1998
	Trevor	0-4-0ST	T. Monk	1998
		0-4-0ST	Clark/Monk	1999
	Invicta	0-4-0	M. Askwith	
		4wPM	M. Stevens	c1997
	Eric	0-4-0PM	Bush/Manning	1998
	Gnu	6wPM	Bush/Manning	1999
		0-6-0BE	Compass House	1999

A pleasant track which is home to a considerable number of locomotives. Be sure to climb to the top of the adjacent windmill while you are there.

MALDON MINIATURE RAILWAY

10¼in gauge

Promenade Park, Maldon, Essex
Telephone: 01621 828795 *OS Ref:* TL861065
Line length: 250yd, end to end
First opened: 1948

No	Name	Type	Builder	Built
		4wRE	M. Harvey	1988

A simple up-and-down ride alongside the amusement park, unique in being electrically powered through a raised third rail. There used to be a Carland Royal Scot here, but when its condition deteriorated the resourceful fairground operator made the present machine using parts of its tender.

PETTITTS ANIMAL ADVENTURE PARK

10¼in gauge

Camphill, Reedham, Norfolk NR13 3UA
Telephone: 01493 700094 *OS Ref:* TG425025 *Operator:* Pettitts
Line length: 500yd, circular *First opened:* 1989 Park entry fee

No	Name	Type	Builder	Built
		S/O 4w-4wDH	Pettitts	1990

Originally 7¼in gauge, the line forms one of the attractions in this animal park. Trains run clockwise from Pettitts Junction.

The Maldon Miniature Railway is unique in being electrically powered via a third rail, as shown here on 21 June 1997.
David Mummery

PLEASUREWOOD HILLS MINIATURE RAILWAY

7¼in gauge

Pleasurewood Hills Theme Park, Corton, nr Lowestoft, Suffolk NR32 5DZ
Telephone: 01502 586000   *OS Ref:* TM543966   *Operator:* Pleasureworld Ltd
Line length: 1,300yd, circular   *First opened:* 1982   Park entry fee

No	Name	Type	Builder	Built
688		6w-6wDH	J. Edwards	1981
723	B. M. Brunning	6w-6wDH	Edwards/Hudson	1984

This line runs from Pleasureworld Hills station through the park area, then through a tunnel and into woodland. There is also a 2ft gauge circuit which crosses the 7¼in gauge, once over a bridge and again on the level. Unusual to find 7¼in gauge working in such a commercial environment.

QUEENS PARK MINIATURE RAILWAY

7¼in gauge

Queens Park, Mablethorpe, Lincolnshire
OS Ref: TF510847   *Operator:* Mr Farrow
Line length: 200yd, circular   *First opened:* 1968

No	Name	Type	Builder	Built
	The Joy Belle	4w-4PM	G. Mawby	1972
11		S/O 4-4wPM	G. Mawby	1976

Before World War 2 Louis Shaw and Percy Harding Kiff operated some notable public 7¼in gauge railways in Mablethorpe. Alas, all one can see today is this simple circle of track in a public park behind the sea wall, running through the tunnel/shed as it goes.

SHERWOOD RAIL

7¼in gauge

East Anglian Railway Museum, Chappel Station, nr Colchester, Essex CO6 2DS
Telephone: 01206 242524   *OS Ref:* TL898289
Operator: East Anglian Railway Museum
Website: http://www.btinternet.com/~earm
Line length: 200yd, end to end   *First opened:* 1991   Site entry fee

No	Name	Type	Builder	Built
	Little John	0-4-0T	J. Chapman	1994
	Romulus	0-4-0WT	Chapman/Martin	1997
		4wPM	J. Chapman	1995

A short line forming an attraction additional to the standard gauge exhibits at the East Anglian Railway Museum.

SOMERLEYTON MINIATURE RAILWAY
7¼in gauge

Somerleyton Hall & Gardens, Somerleyton, Lowestoft, Suffolk NR32 5QQ
Telephone: 01502 730224   *OS Ref:* TM491978   *Operator:* B. Breeze
Website: http://gazetteer.interdart.co.uk/east/visit/SOMHL.htm
Line length: 450yd, circular   *First opened:* 1972   Gardens entry fee

No	Name	Type	Builder	Built
8102	Basil Breeze	2-4-2	King/Breeze	1987
D7026	Somerleyton	4w-4PM	Cromar White	1971
D8000		4w-4PM	B. Breeze	1981

A circular line in the grounds of Somerleyton Hall, which has now celebrated over 25 years of operation. Open Thursdays and Sundays, and peak Tuesdays and Wednesdays, the railway runs from 3pm.

WELLS HARBOUR RAILWAY
10¼in gauge

Beach Road, Wells-next-the-Sea, Norfolk
Telephone: 01328 878871   *OS Ref:* TF915439   *Operator:* M. Want
Website: http://freespace.virgin.net/michael.l/WHR/index.htm
Line length: 1,200yd   *First opened:* 1976

Awaiting departure from the harbour end of the Wells Harbour Railway in August 1998 was 0-6-0DH Densil *and its train. Both locomotive and carriages had been specially built by Alan Keef Ltd earlier in the year.* Bob Darvill

No	Name	Type	Builder	Built
	Edmund Hannay	0-4-2WT	D. King	1971
	(Weasel)	4wPM	D. King	1980
	Densil	S/O 0-6-0DH	A. Keef	1998

This line was the precursor to the Wells & Walsingham Light Railway. It runs from Harbour station at Wells, alongside Beach Road to Pinewoods, forming a useful transport service to and from a caravan site. The little locos must by now have notched up a remarkable mileage. A neat little railway which has recently acquired a new rake of roofed coaches.

WELLS & WALSINGHAM LIGHT RAILWAY   10¼in gauge

Wells-next-the-Sea, Norfolk NR23 1QB
Telephone: 01328 710631   *OS Ref:* TF925430   *Operator:* R. & M. Francis
Website: http://www.broadland.com/fun/wellrail.html
Line length: 4 miles, end to end   *First opened:* 1982

No	Name	Type	Builder	Built
	Norfolk Hero	2-6-0+0-6-2	N. Simkins	1986
		S/O 6wDH	Alan Keef	1985

This is the longest 10¼in gauge railway in the world, and was also the first 10¼in gauge railway to obtain a Light Railway Order. Trains run from the station above Wells-next-the-Sea to Walsingham, along a standard gauge trackbed. *Norfolk Hero* takes the great majority of services, which run daily from Good Friday to the end of September. The railway has an active volunteer support group. Over the winter of 1998/9 major excavations took place which have removed the worst gradients facing Walsingham-bound trains.

Over winter 1998/9 major civil engineering took place at the Wells & Walsingham Light Railway to reduce the maximum gradient approaching Walsingham. The train is seen passing this location in June 1999. John Tidmarsh

Cheshire, Cumbria, Greater Manchester,
Lancashire, Merseyside.

BLACKPOOL ZOO MINIATURE RAILWAY   *15in gauge*

Blackpool Zoo Park, East Park Drive, Blackpool, Lancashire FY3 8PP
Telephone: 01253 765027   *OS Ref:* SD335362
Operator: Blackpool Miniature Railway Co Ltd
Line length: 700yd, end to end   *First opened:* 1972   Zoo entry fee

No	Name	Type	Builder	Built
279		S/O 2-8-0DH	Severn Lamb	1972

A line running within the grounds of the zoo, from Dodge City to Wells Fargo. Trains run every 15min from 10am, March to October; tickets are sold for either single or return journeys.

Trains at the Blackpool Miniature Railway are hauled by this Severn Lamb 'Rio Grande' No 279. Authors' collection

BROOKSIDE MINIATURE RAILWAY   *7¼in gauge*

Brookside Garden Centre, Macclesfield Road, Poynton, Cheshire SK12 1BY
Telephone: 01625 872919   *OS Ref:* SJ927852
Operator: Brookside Garden Centre Ltd
Line length: 800yd, circular   *First opened:* 1990

0-4-2T Princess *on the turntable at the Brookside Miniature Railway on 16 May 1999.* Dave Holroyde

No	Name	Type	Builder	Built
6100	Royal Scot	4-6-0	English Electric	1952
2	Marcus	0-4-0ST	A. Kay	1978
3	Lady Pauline	0-4-2T	A. Kay	1982
	Catherine	0-4-0ST	J. Horsfield	1982
9	Sîan	0-4-0ST	N. Pendlebury	1989
	Princess	0-4-2T	Edgerton/Horsfield	1989
5428		4-6-0	N. Wooler/A. Kay	1996
	Taw	2-6-2T	J. Horsfield	1999
	Jean	0-4-2T	Exmoor Steam Railway	2000
2	Anne	4wPH	McFarlane/Pfeifferbahn	1981
D7031	Temeraire	4-4wPH	Mardyke	1989
2	David	4-4wPH	N. Pendlebury	1991
47632	Brookside	6-6wPH	B. Lomas	1995
5		4w-2PH	J. Horsfield	1996
7		S/O 4wBER	Parkside	1996
D1671		4-6wPH	Lomas/McFarlane	1998
		S/O 4wBER	J. Horsfield	1999

This line runs through a busy garden centre; the scenic route includes two river bridges and a 65ft tunnel. At the station is a replica GWR waiting room, inside which an extensive collection of railwayana is displayed. The steam outline 4wBE locomotive runs on its own track; put a coin in the slot and drive your own train.

CARLISLE MODEL ENGINEERS

5in/7¼in gauge

Hammonds Park, Blackwell Road, Upperby, Carlisle, Cumbria
OS Ref: NY406534   Operator: Carlisle & District Model Engineering Society
Line length: 200yd, circular, elevated   First opened: 1945

No	Name	Type	Builder	Built
	Lady B.	0-4-0T	D. Smallwood	c1980
302	Solway	0-6-0ST	A. Bowron	1987
		4-4-2	W. Oliver	
1994	Santa Fe	4w-4wBE	Oliver/Rae	1994

An elevated circuit in a public park.

CROXTETH PARK MINIATURE RAILWAY

7¼in gauge

Croxteth Hall and Country Park, Croxteth, Liverpool (Merseyside) L12 0HB
Telephone: 0151 228 5311   *OS Ref:* SJ406944
Operator: Forest Model Engineering
Line length: 350yd, circular   *First opened:* 1981

No	Name	Type	Builder	Built
	Estelle	0-4-0T	TMA Engineering	1981
	Mardyke Osprey	4-4wPH	Mardyke	1983
	Mardyke Merlin	6w-6PH	Mardyke	1982

The line runs around a small reserved section of this large country park.

DRAGON MINIATURE RAILWAY

7¼in gauge

**Wyevale Garden Centre, Otterspool, Dooley Lane, Marple, Stockport
(Greater Manchester) SK6 7HE**
OS Ref: SJ937894   *Operator:* B. Lomas
Line length: 250yd, balloon   *First opened:* 1999

No	Name	Type	Builder	Built
	Goliath	0-4-0T	R. Kay	1979
		4wBE	Maxitrak	c1980
D5903	Andrew	4w-4PH	B. Lomas	1985
D1015	Western Champion	6-6wPH	B. Lomas	1997
47338	Flying Dragon	6-6wPH	B. Lomas	1997
		6-6wPH	B. and A. Lomas	1999

Opened as a balloon loop in 1999, this line is to be extended into a dumb-bell. Trains run from Wyevale Junction; nearby are a turntable and three-road shed.

Also running trains on 16 May 1999 was one of the newest lines in this book, the Dragon Miniature Railway at Marple. The locomotive in use was Western Champion. Dave Holroyde

GULLIVERS WORLD RAILWAY   *15in gauge*

Gullivers World, Shackleton Close, Old Hall, Warrington, Cheshire WA5 5YZ
Telephone: 01925 444888   *OS Ref:* SJ589902   *Operator:* D. Phillips
Line length: 500yd, circular   *First opened:* 1989   Park entry fee

No	Name	Type	Builder	Built
		S/O 6+6wDE	Meridian Motioneering	1989

Trains run from the main entrance plaza calling en route at Dinosaurland. There is a bridge over a stream, a footbridge and several level crossings.

HAIGH RAILWAY   *15in gauge*

Haigh Country Park, Haigh, Wigan (Greater Manchester)
Telephone: 01942 832895   *OS Ref:* SD599087
Operator: Wigan Metropolitan Borough Council
Line length: 1 mile, circular   *First opened:* 1986

No	Name	Type	Builder	Built
15	W. Brogan MBE	0-6-0DM	G&SLE	1961
		S/O 0-6-2DH	Alan Keef	1992

This line runs through woodland in the Country Park surrounding Haigh Hall, with stations at Haigh South and Haigh North. Its original stock came from Fairbourne when that railway changed its gauge. A steam outline loco, and coaches, were later purchased from Alan Keef Ltd.

HALTON MINIATURE RAILWAY   *7¼in gauge*

Town Park, Palace Fields, Halton, Runcorn, Cheshire
Telephone: 01928 574396
OS Ref: SJ547815   *Operator:* Halton Miniature Railway Society
Line length: 1 mile, circular   *First opened:* 1980

No	Name	Type	Builder	Built
	Norton Priory School	4w-4PH	Norton Priory School	1980
	Geraldine	0-4-0PH	ICI Widnes	1984
3	Buffalo Bill	S/O 2-8-0PH	A. Bimpson	1984
7		S/O 0-4-0PH	L. Hough	1986

Trains depart from Mousetrap station, near the park entrance, and shortly bear left on to a very long balloon loop. Halfway along this loop is a chord for trains taking only a 'short' journey. There are several passing loops on the way round, for works trains or where locos may pause if need be. This is quite an extensive line; special days are regularly held, during which visiting locomotives often operate.

HAPPY MOUNT EXPRESS   *10¼in gauge*

Happy Mount Park, Bare, Morecambe, Lancashire
OS Ref: SD456653   *Operator:* Mrs P. Woodhouse
Line length: 200yd, circular   *First opened:* c1956

No	Name	Type	Builder	Built
		4-4wPH	E. Sharpe	1982

A simple but long-established line in the grounds of Happy Mount Park, featuring one station and a tunnel.

KNOWSLEY SAFARI PARK RAILWAY *15in gauge*

Knowsley Safari Park, Knowsley Hall, Prescot, Knowsley (Merseyside) L34 4AN
Telephone: 0151 430 9009 *OS Ref:* SJ460936 *Operator:* The Earl of Derby
Line length: 800yd, dumb-bell *First opened:* 1971

No	Name	Type	Builder	Built
		S/O 2-6-0DH	Severn Lamb	1991

This line forms one of the amusement attractions adjacent to the entrance to the Safari Park. Trains cross a bridge then run alongside a lake to a sharply curved balloon loop. Upon their return another tight loop is traversed to reach the station platform.

LAKESIDE MINIATURE RAILWAY *15in gauge*

Marine Lake, Southport, Sefton (Merseyside)
Telephone: 01704 535796 *OS Ref:* SD331174 *Operator:* Spencer & Gittins
Line length: 750yd, end to end *First opened:* 1911

No	Name	Type	Builder	Built
	Red Dragon	4-4-2	Moss/Walker	1991
4468	Duke of Edinburgh	S/O 4-6-2DE	H. Barlow	1948

A scene at Pleasureland station on the Lakeside Miniature Railway, Southport, 3 April 1998. Simon Townsend

No	Name	Type	Builder	Built
2510	Prince Charles	S/O 4-6-2DE	H. Barlow	1954
	Golden Jubilee 1911-1961	S/O 4-6-0DE	H. Barlow	1963
	Princess Anne	6-6wDM	Severn Lamb	1971

One of the two oldest lines in the UK, the Lakeside Miniature Railway can claim a continuous record of service since it was opened originally by Mr Llewellyn, a local postman and shop owner. Trains run from Pleasureland station parallel to the Marine Lake, then curve round underneath the pier to reach Marine Parade. Both termini have two platforms with their own run-round loops, so it is possible to operate all three rakes of stock (two loading, one on the move). The steam loco works on some Saturdays. With its brightly painted stations and stock, this line combines the best of fairground and railway traditions.

LEYLAND MODEL ENGINEERS   5in/7¼in gauge

Worden Park, Leyland, Lancashire PR5 2DS
Telephone: 01772 455580   *OS Ref:* SD538209
Operator: Leyland Society of Model Engineers
Line length: 400yd, end to end   *First opened:* 1998

No	Name	Type	Builder	Built
3157		2-6-2T	K. Wilson	1990
8791	Breakhart	0-4-2ST	D. Croft	1991
	Lancashire Witch	0-4-0ST	F. Halshaw	1994
6027	King Charles III	4-6-0	K. Wilson	1995
		0-6-2T	R. Taylor	1997
		0-4-2T	T. Anderson	1997
No 2	Tarique Shelina	0-6-2T	W. Sumner	1998
	Arthur II	0-6-0PH	A. Foster	c1997

This line runs from a station near to the craft centre (behind the club house and adjacent to the elevated track) uphill on to double track, through open parkland, then crosses the park access road to terminate next to the public car park on Worden Lane. A reversing wye is then used to gain the down line, and return. The track here has been fabricated from steel bars, with recycled plastic being used for sleepers.

LOWTHER MINIATURE RAILWAY   7¼in gauge

Lowther Park, Hackthorpe, Penrith, Cumbria CA10 2HG
Telephone: 01931 712523   *OS Ref:* NY532225   *Operator:* Lowther Park
Line length: 800yd, dumb-bell   *First opened:* 1982   Park entry fee

No	Name	Type	Builder	Built
	Rio Grande	4w-4PH	A. Bimpson	1982
812		6w-6wPH	D. Smallwood	1991

One of many attractions in the leisure park, this line had its own steam loco at one time. The layout is unusual in that the far balloon loop had to be squeezed into a confined space, so it makes a diamond crossing over itself just after the loop points.

MORECAMBE BAY MINIATURE RAILWAY

West End Gardens, Morecambe, Lancashire
OS Ref: SD423636   *Operator:* L. Wynn
Line length: 200yd, circular   *First opened:* 1997

No	Name	Type	Builder	Built
4	Stella Nova	6w-6wPM	R. Yates	1979
5		0-6-0PM	R. Yates	1985
3	Firefly	0-4-0ST	R. Yates	1992

Trains run anticlockwise around this small circuit near to the sea front. The stock here formerly ran on the Netherhall Woodland Railway at Maryport in Cumbria.

PLEASURE BEACH EXPRESS

Pleasure Beach, South Shore, Blackpool, Lancashire FY4 1EZ
Telephone: 01253 341033   *OS Ref:* SD306333
Operator: Blackpool Pleasure Beach
Website: http://www.blackpoolpleasurebeach.co.uk
Line length: 1,000yd, circular   *First opened:* 1934

No	Name	Type	Builder	Built
4472	Mary Louise	S/O 4-6-2DH	Hudswell Clarke	1933
4473	Carol Jean	S/O 4-6-4DH	Hudswell Clarke	1933
6200	The Princess Royal	S/O 4-6-2DH	Hudswell Clarke	1935
		4wDM	A. Keef	1982

Ever-popular among the rides at the Pleasure Beach is the miniature railway, which wends its way past a lake and among the foundations for numerous other rides.

PORT HAVERIGG HOLIDAY VILLAGE RAILWAY

Port Haverigg Holiday Village, Hodbarrow, nr Millom, Cumbria
Telephone: 01229 772880   *OS Ref:* SD171788   *Operators:* R. and S. Attwood
Line length: 400yd, circular   *First opened:* 1997

No	Name	Type	Builder	Built
		0-4-2T	CSM Engineering	1997
		4wPM	V. Crossman	

Trains run from Little Hoddy station around this circuit, which is a sort of irregular rectangle.

THE RAILWAY AGE MINIATURE RAILWAY $7\frac{1}{4}$ in gauge

The Railway Age, Vernon Way, Crewe, Cheshire CW1 2DB
Telephone: 01270 212130   *OS Ref:* SJ709553   *Operator:* The Railway Age
Line length: 600yd, complex   *First opened:* 1992   Site entry fee

No	Name	Type	Builder	Built
		0-6-0T	R. Elmore	c1987
	Jenny	2-4-0ST	Marsh/Rogers	1992
7940		4w-4BE	Severn Lamb	1987
D7003	Norcliff	4w-4PH	ESSE	1993

An unusual line squeezed into the confines of this museum site. Trains leave Crewe (Old Works) terminus, cross over the entrance drive and through a short tunnel to Forge End, where the loco turns and runs round. There is then a straight run between the site perimeter and the prototype Advanced Passenger Train, displayed here, to Midge Bridge, adjacent to Crewe North signalbox, where the loco again turns and runs round, before repeating the journey in the opposite direction.

RAVENGLASS & ESKDALE RAILWAY 15in gauge

Ravenglass, Cumbria CA18 1SW
Telephone: 01229 717171   *OS Ref:* SD086967
Operator: Ravenglass & Eskdale Railway Co Ltd
Website: http://www.ravenglass-railway.co.uk
Line length: 6¾ miles, end to end   *First opened:* 1876

Entering Ravenglass station past the locomotive and carriage sheds on 2 May 1998 is 2-6-2 Northern Rock. *Simon Townsend*

No	Name	Type	Builder	Built
7	River Irt	0-8-2	A. Heywood	1894
11	Bonnie Dundee	0-4-2	Kerr Stuart	1901
	Synolda	4-4-2	Bassett-Lowke	1912
6	River Esk	2-8-2	Davey Paxman	1923
9	River Mite	2-8-2	H. Clarkson	1966
10	Northern Rock	2-6-2	R&ER Co	1976
	Blacolvesley	S/O 4-4-4PM	Bassett-Lowke	1909
ICL No 1		4-4wPM	Ravenglass	1925
	Quarryman	4wPM	Muir Hill	1926
	Perkins	4w-4DM	Muir Hill	1929
ICL9	Cyril	4wDM	Lister	1932
(U2)		4wBE	Greenwood & Batley	1957
21	Les	4wDM	Lister Blackstone	1960
	Shelagh of Eskdale	4-6-4DH	Severn Lamb	1969
1	Scooter	2-2wPMR	R&ER Co	1970
	Silver Jubilee	4-car DMR	R&ER Co	1976
ICL8	Lady Wakefield	4w-4wDH	R&ER Co	1980

The Ravenglass & Eskdale Railway is justifiably marketed as 'the most beautiful train journey in England'. The line was originally 3ft gauge but reopened to 15in gauge in 1914. It was nearly scrapped in 1960, but was saved at the last moment by a group of enthusiasts and since then has been improved out of all recognition by dedicated permanent staff and volunteers. The railway's workshops have extensive facilities and two locomotives have been built here for a railway in Japan. Douglas Ferreira, the manager for many years, was recently awarded the OBE for his outstanding contribution. 0-4-0T *Katie* of 1896 is under restoration here.

Awaiting custom at the Safari Railway on 16 May 1995 was 4wBE Layer. *Its 'safari' livery is somewhat unusual!* Dave Holroyde

SAFARI RAILWAY

South Lakes Wild Animal Park, Dalton-in-Furness, Cumbria LA15 8JR
Telephone: 01229 466086   *OS Ref:* SD238751   *Operator:* D. Gill
Line length: 200yd, end to end   *First opened:* 1995   Park entry fee

No	Name	Type	Builder	Built
	Layer	4wBE	Pfeifferbahn	1990

An out-and-back run from a terminus next to a small lake.

ST ANNES MINIATURE RAILWAY

10¼in gauge

Seafront, St Annes, Lancashire
OS Ref: SD322281
Line length: 700yd, circuit   *First opened:* 1973

No	Name	Type	Builder	Built
	St Annes Express	4w-4DH	Severn Lamb	1973

This line is more or less rectangular, running through the sand dunes, with the tunnel/stock shed at the back of the circuit.

WINDMILL ANIMAL FARM RAILWAY

15in gauge

Red Cat Lane, Burscough, Lancashire L40 1UQ
Telephone: 01704 892282   *OS Ref:* SD427156   *Operator:* A. Moss
Website: http://www.users.globalnet.co.uk/~stownsen
Line length: 400yd, end to end   *First opened:* 1997   Farm entry fee

No	Name	Type	Builder	Built
44		4-4-0	McGarigle	c1902
4	Blue Pacific	4-6-2	N. Guinness	1935
5751	Prince William	4-6-2	G&SLE	1949
		4-4-2	A. Moss	u/c
	Whippit Quick	4w-4DM	Lister	1935
	Silver Jubilee	S/O 4-6-4PE	Smith	1935
	Princess Anne	S/O 4-6w-2DE	H. Barlow	1948
	Duke of Edinburgh	S/O 4-6-2DE	H. Barlow	1950
	(Battison)	S/O 2-6-4DH	S. Battison	1958
4472	Flying Scotsman	S/O 4-6-2 GasH	Artisair	1972
	St Nicholas	S/O 2-8-0 GasH	Severn Lamb	1978
14		2w-2PM	G. Walker	1985
No 1		S/O 4-6-0DM	Jubilee/Volante	1987
		2-2wPMR	A. Moss	1989
D6353	Beaver	4w-4wDM	J. Brown	1998

This line runs from the farm to a picnic area at Lakeview. Rapid progress has been made in building the railway, restoring items of rolling stock and adding covered space to store the ever-growing collection. Public access is occasionally possible to the tracks leading from the new turntable, where it is intended to establish a museum section titled the 15in Gauge Heritage Centre.

AREA 8: NORTH EAST

Durham, North Yorkshire, Northumberland, Redcar & Cleveland, South Yorkshire, Tyne & Wear, West Yorkshire, York.

BEDALE MINIATURE RAILWAY
10¼in gauge

Bedale Hall, Bedale, North Yorkshire
Operator: Wensleydale Railway Company
Line length: 500yd, end to end   *First opened:* 1999

No	Name	Type	Builder	Built
	Pilgrim	0-6-0T	D. King	1981
		2-4w-2DM	Shepperton Metal Products	1968

This new line runs parallel to the Leyburn road, at the north end of Bedale village. It opened on 21 August 1999 and is being extended up to 500 yds in length.

BRADFORD MODEL ENGINEERING SOCIETY
5in/7¼in gauge

Northcliffe Woods, Cliffe Wood Avenue, Shipley, Bradford, West Yorkshire
OS Ref: SE142366   *Operator:* Bradford Model Engineering Society
Line length: 550yd, circular   *First opened:* 1992

No	Name	Type	Builder	Built
962	Tich	0-4-0T	K. Parkinson	1980
51218		0-4-0ST	E. Wright	1981
		4wVBT	R. Spalding	1982
440	Singapore	0-4-0ST	B. Ward	1992
	Idris	0-4-0ST	Martin/Sheard	1993
	Lesley	0-4-2T	P. Whitfield	1993
7105		0-6-0T	B. Ward	1996
	Hercules	0-4-0ST	S. Paley	1997
D7581		4w-4wBE	K. Parkinson	1998
	Dock Authority	4wBE	K. Parkinson	1982
13402		0-6-0PM	D. Brimacombe	1994
	Squirrel	4wBER	R. Spalding	1994
71286	Mossup	4wBE	K. Hartley	c1995
	Pioneer	0-6-0BE	K. Parkinson	1996
60594	Desperate Dan	0-4-0BE	C. Eddison	1998

This line is situated in a woodland park with steaming bays adjacent to the three-road station. The track is dog-bone shaped with testing gradients.

FLAMINGOLAND MINIATURE RAILWAY
15in gauge

Flamingoland Theme Park & Zoo, Kirby Misperton, nr Malton, North Yorkshire YO17 6UX
Telephone: 01653 668287   *OS Ref:* SE779799   *Operator:* Flamingoland Ltd

Website: http://www.flamingoland.co.uk
Line length: 1,000yd, circular   *First opened:* c1969   Park entry fee

No	Name	Type	Builder	Built
7, 278		S/O 2-8-0DH	Severn Lamb	1984

The line is one of many attractions at this leisure park. Trains run clockwise between the two stations over six level crossings.

HEATHERSLAW LIGHT RAILWAY   *15in gauge*

Ford Forge, Heatherslaw, Cornhill on Tweed, Northumberland TD12 4QA
Telephone: 01890 820244   *OS Ref:* NT9343834
Operator: Heatherslaw Light Railway Co Ltd
Line length: 1¼ miles, end to end *First opened:* 1989

No	Name	Type	Builder	Built
	The Lady Augusta	0-4-2	B. Taylor	1989
	Clive	6wDH	N. Smith	1989

Neville Smith's railway runs from the Old Forge along the banks of the River Till past fields and woodland to terminate below the ruins of Etal Castle. Trains depart hourly, and are normally steam hauled, from Easter to the end of October (closed Fridays in October). An 0-6-0 is planned.

HEMSWORTH WATER PARK
MINIATURE RAILWAY   *7¼in gauge*

Hemsworth Water Park, Wakefield Road, Kinsley, nr Hemsworth,
Wakefield (West Yorkshire)
Telephone: 01977 617617   *OS Ref:* SE421147   *Operator:* N. Bartle
Line length: 300yd, circular   *First opened:* 1993   Park entry fee

No	Name	Type	Builder	Built
	Lucy	0-4-2T	J. Stubbs	1991
	Christopher	S/O 4w-2PH	J. Horsfield	1990

This line has one station, with a spur to a turntable and three-road shed. A trip is two circuits.

KIRKLEES LIGHT RAILWAY   *15in gauge*

Park Mill Way, Long Lane, Clayton West, Kirklees (West Yorkshire) HD8 9XJ
Telephone: 01484 865727   *OS Ref:* SE258112
Operator: Kirklees Light Railway Co Ltd
Line length: 3¼ miles, end to end *First opened:* 1991

No	Name	Type	Builder	Built
	Fox	2-6-2T	B. Taylor	1987
	Badger	0-6-4ST	B. Taylor	1991
	Hawk	0-4-0+0-4-0	B. Taylor	1998
7		S/O 2-2wPH	B. Taylor	1991
	Jay	4wDH	B. Taylor	1992

This line has been built to re-create the atmosphere of a fussy little branch line. Running from Clayton West along the embankment of a standard gauge trackbed, the railway has now been extended for a further two miles to Shelley, the longer journey including a ¼-mile tunnel. A new station building has also been constructed, and a Kitson Meyer locomotive (*Hawk*) completed. Trains run hourly from 11am on weekends and bank/public holidays all year round, and daily from Whitsun to the end of August. An Avonside geared bogie locomotive is under construction.

On 17 June 1998 0-4-0+0-4-0 Hawk *worked an evening special for the Narrow Gauge Railway Society along the Kirklees Light Railway. It is seen running round the train at Shelley.* John K. Williams

LAKESHORE RAILROAD

9½in gauge

South Marine Park, South Shields, South Tyneside (Tyne & Wear)
OS Ref: NZ373674
Line length: 550yd, circular
Operators: D. Proudlock and M. Henderson
First opened: 1972

No	Name	Type	Builder	Built
3440	Mountaineer	4-6-2	Jennings/Proudlock/Wakefield	1968
27	Adiela	2-6-2	Bell/Burgoyne	c1939
			reb. Proudlock/Henderson	1976

This line runs around the lake in this public park, with numerous footpath crossings. Both locos are notable scale models, *Mountaineer* being ⅛th scale of an Atchison, Topeka & Santa Fe prototype, and *Adiela* a ¼ scale of a Ferrocarril Nacional del Magdalena (Colombia) locomotive. A 'Wabash' 4-6-4 is under construction.

LAKESIDE RAILWAY

10¼in gauge

Roundhay Park, Roundhay, Leeds (West Yorkshire)
OS Ref: SE331384   *Operator:* H. Kershaw
Line length: 600yd, dumb-bell   *First opened:* 1989

No	Name	Type	Builder	Built
		4wPM	Clitheroe/Stanhope/Kershaw	1987

A line with rustic charm, running through trees adjacent to the lake at the north end of this large public park.

LIGHTWATER VALLEY MINIATURE RAILWAY

15in gauge

Lightwater Valley Theme Park, North Stanley, nr Ripon, North Yorkshire HG4 3HT
Telephone: 01765 635321   *OS Ref:* SE285756
Operator: Lightwater Leisure Ltd
Website: http://www.lightwatervalley.co.uk/pages/home.htm
Line length: 1,300yd, circular   *First opened:* 1979   Park entry fee

No	Name	Type	Builder	Built
11	Yvette	4-4-0	E. Craven	1946
7, 278		S/O 2-8-0DH	Severn Lamb	1979

A well-engineered line carrying visitors from one side of the park to the other. The steam locomotive is privately owned.

METAL BRIDGE RAILWAY

7¼in gauge

The Poachers Pocket Public House, Bridge Street, Metal Bridge, nr Ferryhill, Co Durham DH6 5LQ
Telephone: 01740 654268   OS Ref: NZ300351
Line length: 100yd, circular   First opened: 1994

No	Name	Type	Builder	Built
0123	Princess Claire	4wPH	Harvey/Maxitrak	1990

The line is a circuit in the beer garden of the pub, which is adjacent to the main East Coast railway line.

NEWBY HALL MINIATURE RAILWAY

10¼in gauge

Newby Hall Gardens, Skelton on Ure, nr Ripon, North Yorkshire HG4 5AE
Telephone: 01423 322583   *OS Ref:* SE347675   *Operator:* Hon R. Compton
Website: http://www.newbyhall.co.uk
Line length: 1,000yd, dumb-bell   *First opened:* 1971   Gardens entry fee

No	Name	Type	Builder	Built
6100	Royal Scot	4-6-0	S. Battison	1953
	Countess de Grey	4w-4 GasH	Severn Lamb	1973

This line has an attractive little station more or less in the middle of the track. Trains run parallel to the River Ure before reaching the first loop which includes a tunnel. On the return journey, trains run through the station nonstop before crossing a bridge and entering the second loop which passes through a wood.

NORTH BAY RAILWAY
20in gauge

Northstead Manor Gardens, Scarborough, North Yorkshire
Telephone: 01723 372351   *OS Ref:* TA035898
Operator: Scarborough Borough Council
Line length: 1,300yd, end to end   *First opened:* 1931

No	Name	Type	Builder	Built
1931	*Neptune*	S/O 4-6-2DH	Hudswell Clarke	1931
1932	*Triton*	S/O 4-6-2DH	Hudswell Clarke	1932

Trains depart from Peasholm station, dive beneath the water chute and through a short tunnel, before swinging out to gain the sea front at the halfway passing loop, whence they continue to Scalby Mills. There is now a turntable at Scalby Mills but at Peasholm locomotives run round and turn by means of a sharply curved loop. This is a professionally run line performing a useful task in transporting visitors to and from the attractions at Scalby Mills. The long-established line is under threat from a new development; let us hope that it continues for another 50 years.

ORCHARD FARM LAKESIDE RAILWAY
10¼in gauge

Orchard Farm Holiday Village, Hunmanby, North Yorkshire YO14 0PU
Telephone: 01723 891582   *OS Ref:* TA104778   *Operator:* A. Hunneybell
Line length: 500yd, dumb-bell   *First opened:* 1995

No	Name	Type	Builder	Built
		0-4-0ST	A. Hunneybell/	1999
	Honeywell	4w-4DH	A. Hunneybell/IBC Welding	1992

A recently constructed line in the grounds of this caravan park. It boasts an attractive station with overall roof, from where trains head out and around the lake. *Honeywell*, an HST look-alike, is the usual motive power.

This battery electric 'Pullman' set shows an interesting and original approach to 7¼in gauge rolling stock, at the Pugneys Light Railway on 16 May 1999. Dave Holroyde

PUGNEYS LIGHT RAILWAY

7¼in gauge

Pugneys Country Park, Durkar, Wakefield (West Yorkshire)
Telephone: 01924 302360   *OS Ref:* SE324179
Operators: A. Sowden and J. Pinder
Line length: 750yd, balloon   *First opened:* 1998

No	Name	Type	Builder	Built
		4-4w-4w-4-4BER	A. Sowden/J. Pinder	1996
4304		4w-4w-4-4-4BER	A. Sowden/J. Pinder	1998

The line runs from Pugneys Lakeside along the edge of the lake via a passing loop to Pugneys Central, and then around a balloon loop. A S/O PH Garratt and 2-6-2T are under construction for this line.

RIO GRANDE EXPRESS

10¼in gauge

Saville Bros Garden Centre, Garforth Cliff, Garforth, Leeds (West Yorkshire)
Telephone: 0113 286 2183   *OS Ref:* SE416319   *Operator:* Saville Bros Ltd
Line length: 900yd, dumb-bell   *First opened:* 1978

No	Name	Type	Builder	Built
278		S/O 2-8-0PH	Severn Lamb	1978

This railway is the only one we have yet seen with its station, Cactus Junction, inside a glasshouse. The journey features a bridge, a tunnel and two level crossings.

ROSEHIP VALLEY RAILWAY

12¼in gauge

Walkley's Canalside Mill, Hebden Bridge, Calderdale (West Yorkshire) HX7 8NH
Telephone: 01422 842061   *OS Ref:* SE002265
Line length: 300yd, end to end   *First opened:* 1998

No	Name	Type	Builder	Built
	Santa Fe	4w-4wPH	Chapman/Reen	c1995

Trains run back and forth alongside the car park, which is adjacent to the River Calder. There are three stations; the line passes through a shed/tunnel en route.

RUSWARP MINIATURE RAILWAY

7¼in gauge

The Carrs, Ruswarp, nr Whitby, North Yorkshire
OS Ref: NZ885088
Line length: 700yd, circular   *First opened:* 1990

No	Name	Type	Builder	Built
	Danny	2-4-2	D. & G. Sims	1992
	Emily	2-4-2T	D. & G. Sims	1994

This line is a convoluted circuit, twisted round upon itself on land adjacent to the River Esk. Both the locos were built by Doug Sims and are minimum gauge types, *Emily* being 'sit in'.

A short train at the Saltburn Miniature Railway on 22 May 1999 was headed by Prince Charles. Simon Townsend

SALTBURN MINIATURE RAILWAY

15in gauge

Cat Nab, Saltburn, Redcar & Cleveland
Telephone: 01287 633396 *OS Ref:* NZ667216
Operator: Saltburn Miniature Railway Assoc.
Line length: 700yd, end to end *First opened:* 1947

No	Name	Type	Builder	Built
	Prince Charles	S/O 4-6-2DE	H. Barlow	1953
	George Outhwaite	S/O 0-4-0DH	Saltburn Miniature Railway Assoc	1994

A long-established line running from a coastal terminus at Cat Nab into the Italian Gardens. Its future now seems assured since it was taken over by a group of enthusiasts some years ago.

SHIBDEN MINIATURE RAILWAY

10¼in gauge

Shibden Park, Listers Road, Halifax, Calderdale (West Yorkshire) HX3 6XG
Telephone: 01422 352246 *OS Ref:* SE108262 *Operator:* K. Norris
Line length: 700yd, circular *First opened:* 1983

No	Name	Type	Builder	Built
No 1	Ivor	0-6-0ST	B. Taylor	1984
	Ivan	4w-4wDE	B. Taylor	1985

This railway is situated at the valley bottom of a large park that includes a museum in Shibden Hall. The track loops around between a stream and the side of the valley through woodland and a picnic area. There is a tunnel and two bridges over the stream.

SOUTH GARDEN MINIATURE RAILWAY

7¼in gauge

National Railway Museum, Leeman Road, York, North Yorkshire YO26 4XJ
Telephone: 01904 686263   *OS Ref:* SE593519
Operator: National Railway Museum
Website: http://www.nmsi.ac.uk/nrm/html/home-pb/home.htm
Line length: 200yd, end to end   *First opened:* 1996   Museum entry fee

No	Name	Type	Builder	Built
	Taw	2-6-2T	Milner Engineering	1980
	Margaret	0-4-0ST	National Railway Museum	1981
	Lashin' Middlin	0-4-0ST	R. Gibbon	1987
	John	6wPH	R. Greatrex	1997
	Helen	6wPH	R. Greatrex	1998

This modest line has been laid in the South Yard of the National Railway Museum; out and back with a station at the middle of the run. Some of the above locomotives may at times be displayed among the other large-scale models within the museum.

THORNES PARK RAILWAY

7¼in gauge

Thornes Park, Horbury Road, Wakefield, West Yorkshire
OS Ref: SE323200
Operator: Wakefield Society of Model and Experimental Engineers
Line length: 800yd, circular   *First opened:* c1974

No	Name	Type	Builder	Built
	Ken Rosewarne	4-4-0	Leeds Grammar School	c1971
	Linda	0-4-0ST	J. Stubbs	1978
	Edward	0-4-0WT	A. Bennett	1986
4082		0-6-0T	D. Lewin	c1987
1007		4-8-4	J. Stubbs	1988
70008	Black Prince	4-6-2	A. Bickerstaffe	1989
12	Alice	2-4-2	J. Stubbs	1995
	Charles	0-4-0ST	P. Carr	1995
	Debra	0-4-0ST	K. Sabey	1996
13	Hiawatha	4-6-4	J. Stubbs/I. Hickling	1997
14	Petunia	0-4-2T	Stubbs/Hurley	1997
415	Li'l Abner	2-8-0	J. Stubbs	1998
16	Victoria	0-4-2T	J.Stubbs	1999

This line is a circle wrapped across itself by means of a diamond crossing. It has an impressive stable of motive power. Trains run every Sunday afternoon.

WEST RIDING SMALL LOCOMOTIVE SOCIETY

7¼in gauge

Blackgates, Bradford Road, Tingley, nr Wakefield (West Yorkshire) WF3 1RU
OS Ref: SE291261   *Operator:* West Riding Small Locomotive Society Ltd
Line length: 250yd, circular   *First opened:* 1986

No	Name	Type	Builder	Built
	Bernstein	0-4-0ST	P. Clayton	1989
825		4-6-0	Bennett/Pickup	1992

No	Name	Type	Builder	Built
5305	Alderman A. E. Draper	4-6-0	Clayton/Appleton	1993
	June D.	0-6-0PT	B. Deas	c1997
	Herdwick	0-4-0T	C. Todd	1999
819		4-6-0	Bennett/Pickup	1999
51082	Stacey Marie	0-6-0PM	C. Bradley	c1984

The circuit here has an elevated track just inside it; there is a tunnel just before the station.

WHORLTON LIDO RAILWAY

15in gauge

Whorlton Lido, Whorlton, nr Barnard Castle, Co Durham
Telephone: 01833 627397 *OS Ref:* NZ106146
Operator: Mrs Watson
Line length: 750yd, dumb-bell *First opened:* 1971 Park entry fee

No	Name	Type	Builder	Built
	Wendy	4-4wDM	R. Dunn/Coleby Simkins	1972

Whorlton Lido is a popular beauty spot. The line was built when it was owned by the Dunn family; its steam locos have now gone elsewhere, but *Wendy* still operates here.

WORTLEY TOP FORGE MINIATURE RAILWAY

5in/7¼in gauge

Wortley Top Forge, Wortley, nr Stocksbridge, Sheffield (South Yorkshire) S35 7DN
Telephone: 0114 288 7576 *OS Ref:* SK295999
Operator: Wortley Top Forge Model Engineers
Line length: 500yd, circular *First opened:* 1980

No	Name	Type	Builder	Built
	Rusalka	0-4-2T	J. Sykes	1986
	Bethany	0-4-0	Pratt/Oughton	1978
	Emily	0-4-0	Pettifer/Walton	1979
	Edward Thomas	0-4-2ST	B. Donn	1990
	Darlow	0-4-0WT	Darlow/Donn	1993
	Langsett	0-6-0ST	E. Wilson	1993
	Wild Aster	0-4-0ST	C. Farrar	1993
	Laura George	0-4-0	A. Parsons	c1996
	Katie	0-4-0	G. Walker	1999
	Mythago	0-4-0ST	S. Hazlewood	1999
	Yorkie	0-4-0PM	L. Donn	1988
		0-4-0PM	B. Morton	1989
2049		4w-4wBER	A. Buttress	1997
		4wPH	V. Harkin	1998
	Skimbleshanks	4wBE	P. Stokes	1998

This line is a long thin circuit, situated between the forge and the River Don. The station at Wortley Central is broadly in the middle. Part of the track is interlaced with a 16in gauge industrial line.

AREA 9: SCOTLAND

Angus, Argyll & Bute, Dumfries & Galloway, Fife, Highland, South Ayrshire and South Lanarkshire.

AGNEW PARK MINIATURE RAILWAY

7¼in gauge

Agnew Park, Sea Front, Stranraer, Dumfries & Galloway
Telephone: 01776 702151   *OS Ref:* NX056612
Operator: Dumfries and Galloway Council
Line length: 800yd, circular   *First opened:* 1997

No	Name	Type	Builder	Built
		6wPH	R. Greatrex	1997

The railway follows contours around the boating lake, crazy golf course and children's playground, with a station adjacent to the Agnew Park Pavilion. There is a spur to a turntable and a four-road shed. The location has extensive sea views down Loch Ryan to Ailsa Craig and Arran.

AYR MINIATURE RAILWAY

10¼in gauge

Peter Pan Playground, The Promenade, Ayr, South Ayrshire
OS Ref: NS332221   *Operator:* South Ayrshire District Council
Line length: 400yd, circular   *First opened:* 1968

No	Name	Type	Builder	Built
	Ayr Princess	6w-6PH	Severn Lamb	1968

A Severn Lamb 'Western' class operates on this short line. Trains run clockwise from Fort station, passing through the tunnel/shed en route.

BRECHIN CASTLE CENTRE RAILWAY

10¼in gauge

Brechin Castle Garden Centre, Haughmuir, Brechin, Angus DD9 6RL
Telephone: 01356 626813   *OS Ref:* NO577600   *Operator:* Lord Ramsay
Line length: 300yd, circular   *First opened:* 1997

No	Name	Type	Builder	Built
		4-4wPH	A. Binning	1988

This line is a simple circuit next to the lake.

CRAIGTOUN MINIATURE RAILWAY

15in gauge

Craigtoun Park, St Andrews, Fife KY16 8NX
Telephone: 01334 473666   *OS Ref:* NO482141   *Operator:* Fife Council
Line length: 400yd, circular   *First opened:* c1960

No	Name	Type	Builder	Built
278	Ivor	S/O 2-8-0DH	Severn Lamb	1976

This railway was altered in 1995/6 from an end to end line to a circuit around the lake. There are numerous level crossings en route.

KERR'S MINIATURE RAILWAY

10¼in gauge

West Links Park, Arbroath, Angus
Telephone: 01241 879249
Line length: 350yd, end to end
OS Ref: NO629401
First opened: 1935
Operator: M. Kerr

No	Name	Type	Builder	Built
2005	King George VI	4-6-2	H. Bullock	1935
3007	Firefly	0-6-0	H. Bullock	1936
	Tich	0-4-0T	D. Watt	1994
9872	Auld Reekie	S/O 4-4-2PM	W. Jennings	1935
	Ivor	0-6-0PM	Coleby Simkins	1972
25081		4-4wPM	M. Eastwood	1981
D7594		4-4wPM	M. Eastwood	1992
	Rusty	2-2wBE	D. Watt	1999

'KMR' is one of Britain's oldest miniature railways and has carried over 1¾ million passengers. It runs there and back adjacent to ScotRail's main line between Aberdeen and Edinburgh, passing through a tunnel as it goes. Matthew and his team of volunteers maintain the line in immaculate condition, its straight track being renowned for not having a stone of ballast out of place. Children's rides are also given in a miniature bus and fire engine when the railway is open.

Trains behind Firefly *or* Ivor *are on offer to passengers at Kerr's Miniature Railway on 22 September 1996.* Dave Holroyde

LOCH FYNE MINIATURE RAILWAY

John Smith Memorial Gardens, Ardrishaig, Argyll & Bute
OS Ref: NM848856   *Operator:* Loch Fyne Miniature Railway Society
Line length: 300yd, end to end   *First opened:* 1998

No	Name	Type	Builder	Built
4472	Flying Scotsman	4-6-2	Carland Engineering	1948
		0-4-0PH	Roanoke	1999

An out-and-back run from the brick-built engine shed here.

MULL & WEST HIGHLAND NARROW GAUGE RAILWAY

Craignure, Isle of Mull, Argyll & Bute PA65 6AY
Telephone: 01680 812494   *OS Ref:* NM724369
Operator: Mull & West Highland Narrow Gauge Railway Co Ltd
Website: http://www.zynet.co.uk/mull/rail/
Line length: 1 mile, end to end   *First opened:* 1993

No	Name	Type	Builder	Built
196	Waverley	4-4-2	D. Curwen	1948
	Lady of the Isles	2-6-4T	R. Marsh	1981
	Victoria	2-6-2T	D. Vere	1993
NM2		4-4wPM	A. Allcock	1973
	Glen Auldyn	4w-4wDH	R. Davies	1986
		4w-4wDH	D. Vere	1999

Trains run from the station at Craignure Old Pier, near to the terminal of the ferry from Oban, to Torosay Castle and gardens. En route to the passing loop at Tarmstedt can be seen panoramic views of Ben Nevis, the Glencoe mountains, the island of Lismore and Duart Castle. The line then enters a more heavily graded section through woodland. This 'minimum gauge' line is Scotland's only island passenger railway.

2-6-2T Victoria *has been posed on the turntable at Craignure, Mull Railway, ready for this photograph on 23 September 1993.* N. R. Knight

NESS ISLANDS RAILWAY

7¼in gauge

Whin Island, Bught Park, Inverness, Highland
OS Ref: NH655433   *Operator:* I. Young
Line length: 800yd, dumb-bell   *First opened:* 1983

No	Name	Type	Builder	Built
	Uncle John	0-4-2T	R. Marsh	1978
47548	Uncle Frank	6w-6wDH	Mardyke	1989
D7071	Uncle Louis	4w-4wDH	Mardyke	1990
		4w-2PH	R. Greatrex	1999

Britain's most northerly public miniature railway is situated on the western edge of Inverness, on an island consisting mainly of a children's play park and boating lake. The line is a dumb-bell folded over on top of itself, with the station on the C-shaped single line in the middle. The steam loco normally operates at weekends.

STRATHAVEN MINIATURE RAILWAY

5in/7¼in gauge

George Allan Park, Three Stones Road, Strathaven, South Lanarkshire
OS Ref: NS700448   *Operator:* Strathaven Model Society Ltd
Line length: 450yd, circular   *First opened:* 1949

No	Name	Type	Builder	Built
1949		2-6-0	Scott/Hamilton	1947
77020		2-6-0	D. Horsfall	1984
	Lady Joy	0-4-0ST	Chalmers/Pucci	c1984
6126	Sans Pareil	4-6-0	A. Glaze	1986
1419	Elizabeth	4-6-0	J. Powrie	1988
8402		2-8-0	Scarrott/Howard	1989
65320	Clan Stewart	2-8-2	J. Powrie	1994
		0-4-0ST	K. Johnson	c1994
	Abberton	4wPH	Pfeifferbahn	1992
D5571		6w-6wBE	Compass House	1997

This line is a double circuit with the two routes connected by a crossing next to the station. Trains run anticlockwise from Strathaven Central station. There is an elevated track within the main circuits.

At the Aberaeron Wildlife and Leisure Park on 7 June 1998 the train awaiting service was headed by the 4wPH locomotive. R. W. A. Jones

AREA 10: WALES

Carmarthenshire, Ceredigion, Conwy, Denbighshire, Gwynedd, Pembrokeshire.

ABERAERON WILDLIFE AND LEISURE PARK RAILWAY

7¼in gauge

Aberaeron Wildlife and Leisure Park, Blaen y Waun, Aberaeron, Ceredigion SA46 0LA
Telephone: 01545 570766
Line length: 500yd, complex

OS Ref: SN481622
First opened: 1990   Park entry fee

No	Name	Type	Builder	Built
		4-4wPH	Pfeifferbahn	1979
		4wPH	Pfeifferbahn	1984

This line is formed from two linked circuits, each having a station. A long spur leads to a turntable and five-road shed.

CONWY VALLEY RAILWAY

7¼in and also 15in gauge

Conwy Valley Railway Museum, Old Station, Betws-y-coed, Conwy LL24 0AL
Telephone: 01690 710568
7¼in gauge; 950yd
15in gauge; 500yd, end to end

OS Ref: SH796565   *Operator:* C. Cartwright
First opened: 1979
First opened: 1991

No	Name	Type	Builder	Built
7¼in gauge:				
6201	Princess Elizabeth	4-6-2	D. and A. Barton	c1959
402	Shoshone	2-8-0	Milner Engineering	1977
407	Old Rube	2-8-0	Milner Engineering	1983
	Sîan	0-4-2T	K. Humphreys	1988
D7000		4w-4PM	T. Smith	1967
403	Prince of the Parsenn	0-6-0+0-6-0BE	Pfeifferbahn	1987
6641		4-4wPH	R. Greatrex	1990
7		S/O 4wBER	Parkside	1995
15in gauge:				
		4w-4wWER	Wall/Cartwright	1989
70000	Britannia	4-6-2	Longfleet/TMA	1988

The Conwy Valley Railway Museum can be found over the footbridge from Betws-y-coed. Within the museum is a fine scale model of *Britannia*, along with interesting exhibits including other large-scale models. Outside the museum is an extensive and ever-popular 7¼in gauge railway, basically a dumb-bell layout with the two loops interlaced. The line crosses behind the museum, protected by automatic level crossing barriers. The 15in gauge line is worked by an open tram, taking power from an overhead line using a traditional trolley pole. The 4wBER operates on a separate track; put a coin in the slot and drive your own train. The museum, 7¼in gauge line and tramway are complementary attractions, all in a popular location.

The 7¼in gauge station at the Conwy Valley Railway Museum is just opposite that for the main line branch to Blaenau Ffestiniog. Robin Butterell

The half-sized narrow gauge train with Welsh mountain backdrop can only make this the Fairbourne & Barmouth Railway. Simon Townsend

FAIRBOURNE & BARMOUTH STEAM RAILWAY

12¼in gauge

Beach Road, Fairbourne, Gwynedd LL38 2PZ
Telephone: 01341 250362   *OS Ref:* SH616128
Operator: North Wales Coast Light Railway Ltd
Website: http://www.tourism-services.ndirect.co.uk/fairrail
Line length: 1¾ miles, end to end   *First opened:* 1916

No	Name	Type	Builder	Built
4	Sherpa	0-4-0ST	Milner Engineering	1978
E759	Yeo	2-6-2T	D. Curwen	1978
5	Russell	2-6-4T	Milner Engineering	1979
2	Beddgelert	0-6-4T	D. Curwen	1979
6	Lilian Walter	4w-4wDM	G&SLE	1961
7	Gwril	4wBE	Fairbourne	1987

This line originated in 1896 as a 2ft gauge horse tramway. In 1916 the tramway was relaid to 15in gauge. In this form the line eked out a humble existence until the mid-1950s when a decade of improvements commenced. In 1984 a new owner took over and the line was progressively transformed, including regauging to 12¼in in 1986. Trains are now mostly hauled by one of four half-size replicas of 2ft gauge steam locomotives, which make a pleasing sight with the distinctive rakes of red coaches. The present owners bought the railway in 1995.

The line runs from Fairbourne station alongside Beach Road and through the sand dunes passing the station at Gorsafawddachaidraigodanheddogleddollonpenrhynareurdraethceredigion, formerly named Golf Halt. Trains often pass at the midway loop, before continuing next to the road, then entering a long tunnel and emerging on the far side of the dunes, finally swinging round into Porth Penrhyn. From here it is only a short ferry ride to Barmouth.

GREEN DRAGON RAILWAY

7¼in gauge

Teifi Valley Railway, Henllan, nr Newcastle Emlyn, Ceredigion SA44 5TD
Telephone: 01559 371077   *OS Ref:* SN359407   *Operator:* Teifi Valley Railway
Website: http://members.aol.com/WalesRails/tvr.ht
Line length: 250yd, end to end   *First opened:* 1998

No	Name	Type	Builder	Built
	Sir Geraint Evans	0-4-0ST	J. Horsfield	1989
	(Claris)	0-6-2ST	S. Browne	1990
	Emlyn	4wPM	S. Browne	1990
	Epod	0-6-0PH	F. Bond	1998

This line is an ancillary attraction to the 2ft gauge trains of the Teifi Valley Railway. Trains run from Henllan high-level station.

LLWYFAN CERRIG MINIATURE RAILWAY

7¼in gauge

Llwyfan Cerrig Station, Gwili Railway, nr Carmarthen, Carmarthenshire SA32 6HT
Telephone: 01267 230666   *OS Ref:* SN405258   *Operator:* F. Bond
Line length: 200yd, end to end   *First opened:* 1993

No	Name	Type	Builder	Built
	Ddraig Ddu	0-4-0VBT	R. Harrison	c1978
	Jason	0-4-0T	Page Engineering	1992
	Michael	0-4-0PH	Page Engineering	1992
		0-6-0PH	F. Bond	1997

The only public access to this line is by train, on the Gwili Railway from Bronwydd Arms station; the 7¼in gauge line operates on every day that Gwili trains are timetabled. *Jason* and *Michael* both ran at the National Garden Festival Wales in 1992 before the line here was

OAKWOOD MINIATURE RAILWAY
15in gauge built

Oakwood Adventure Park, Canaston Bridge, Narberth, Pembrokeshire SA67 8DE
Telephone: 01834 85373   *OS Ref:* SN072124   *Operator:* Oakwood Leisure Ltd
Line length: 1,100yd, circuit   *First opened:* 1987   Park entry fee

No	Name	Type	Builder	Built
	Lindy-Lou	S/O 0-8-0DH	Severn Lamb	1972
	Lenka	4-4wDHR	Severn Lamb	1973
278		S/O 0-8-0PH	Severn Lamb	1976
	Lorna	4-4wDHR	Goold Bros	1989

This line serves as a transport system from the entrance to the main part of the adventure park. Passengers travel from Oakwood station, serving the entrance, around to Market Street station, where they disembark. When leaving the park they return around a much shorter section of the circuit.

RHYL MINIATURE RAILWAY
15in gauge

Marine Lake Leisure Park, Wellington Road, Rhyl, Denbighshire
Telephone: (H): 01352 759109   *OS Ref:* SH999807   *Operator:* L. Hughes
Website: http://www.users.globalnet.co.uk/~stownsen
Line length: 1,700yd, circular   *First opened:* 1911

No	Name	Type	Builder	Built
101	Joan	4-4-2	A. Barnes	1920
	Clara	S/O 0-4-2DM	G&SLE	1961
		4wDM	Lister	1938
KD1		4-4w-4-4w-4DER	Rapido Rail	1983

This line shares (with the Lakeside Miniature Railway, Southport) the honour of running on Britain's oldest miniature railway site. The original railway here closed in 1969 but was relaid in 1978, and then again in 1998. *Joan* operates, weather permitting, on most Sundays from Whit to early September, and on peak Thursdays; on these occasions the ride round the Marine Lake is just as you would have found it in 1920. Two further Barnes Atlantics, *Railway Queen* and *Michael*, are also owned by Les Hughes but are presently on display at James Pringle Weavers, Llanfair PG, Anglesey.

Waldenburg hauling a train at the Belfast & County Down Miniature Railway on 18 September 1999. Dave Holroyde

AREA 11: IRELAND

BELFAST & COUNTY DOWN MINIATURE RAILWAY

7¼in gauge

Upper Gransha Road, Donaghadee, Ards (County Down)
Telephone (H): 028 9188 2013   *OS Ref:* J547761
Operator: Belfast & County Down Miniature Railway Society
Line length: 1,000yd, complex   *First opened:* 1994

No	Name	Type	Builder	Built
6	Waldenburg	0-6-0T	L. Nelson	1981
	Finn MacCool	0-4-2	TMA Engineering	1986
25	Winifred	0-4-0ST	D. Tedford	1989
	Wren	0-4-0ST	S. Williamson	1992
		6wPH	Greatrex/Tedford	1999
		0-4-0PH	Roanoke	1998
	Helios	0-4-2DH	Roanoke	1999
	William John	6wPH	Greatrex/Allen	1999
	Electra	4wPH	Roanoke	1999
21		0-4-0+4PMR	H. McCauley	1999

The line comprises a circuit off which there is an additional loop. There is one station at Drumawhey Junction, a tunnel and a rail-over-rail bridge. A turntable and six-road shed have recently been added.

CARNFUNNOCK COUNTRY PARK MINIATURE RAILWAY

7¼in gauge

Carnfunnock Country Park, Coast Road, Drains Bay, Ballygally, Larne BT40 2QG
Telephone: 028 2827 0541   *OS Ref:* D384067   *Operator:* P. Johnston
Line length: 650yd, dumb-bell   *First opened:* 1998

No	Name	Type	Builder	Built
43072		4w-4PM	R. Powers	1994
	Colonel Bogey	6wPH	R. Greatrex	1997

Passengers board at Carnfunnock Halt, which is on one of the loops of this dumb-bell layout.

COLERAINE MODEL ENGINEERS

3½in/5in/7¼in gauge

Turnakibbock, Damhead, Coleraine (County Londonderry)
OS Ref: C895303   *Operator:* Coleraine & District Society of Model Engineers Ltd
Line length: 150yd, circular

No	Name	Type	Builder	Built
	Hercules	0-4-2T	T. Snoxell	c1972
		0-4-2T	R. Morrison	1978
	Taurus	0-4-0T	T. Snoxell	1984
		0-4-2T	R. Morrison	c1985
		0-4-2T	R. Morrison	c1989
001	Hermes	0-6-0T	M. Getty	1998
No 4	Hydraulic	0-6-0PH	K. Boyd	1992
		0-6-0PH	K. Boyd	c1995
08	Red Arrow	0-6-0PH	R. Morrison	1999

This line is a simple circuit from Turnakibbock station. Access to the club house is gained via a footbridge over the track. A turntable leads to several steaming bays.

CULTRA LIGHT RAILWAY

7¼in gauge

Ulster Folk and Transport Museum, Cultra, nr Holywood, North Down BT18 0EU
Telephone: 028 9042 8428   *OS Ref:* J418809
Operator: Model Engineers Society of Northern Ireland
Line length: 350yd, circular   *First opened:* 1985   Museum entry fee

No	Name	Type	Builder	Built
	Marian	0-4-0ST	J. Conn	c1989
	Betty	0-4-0ST	MESNI	c1993
(D7016)	Sir Myles	4w-4PM	Cromar White	1969
		4wPM	T. D. Wilson	1982
	Wavin (NI) Ltd	0-6-0PH	R. Greatrex	1991

The line here runs in and out of a walled garden. The station at Cultra Central has footbridge access to the elevated 3¼in/5in gauge tracks inside the circuit.

Pickie Puffer *photographed on 7 August 1996, passing the shed roads to the left on the Pickie Family Fun Park Railway (page 86).*
Dave Holroyde

JOHN F. KENNEDY ARBORETUM MINIATURE RAILWAY

7¼in gauge

John F. Kennedy Arboretum, New Ross, nr Canpile, County Wexford
Telephone: 00353 51 388171   *OS Ref:* S725184
Operator: J. F. Kennedy Arboretum
Line length: 450yd, circular   *First opened:* 1990

No	Name	Type	Builder	Built
	Santa Fe	4-4wPH	B. Meyler	1989

This is an irregular circuit, running from a single station.

The John F. Kennedy Arboretum Miniature Railway features a Santa Fe locomotive and coaches with painted 'windows', seen here in 1993.
Rod Bryant

LEISURELAND EXPRESS

15in gauge

Sea front, Salthill, Galway, County Galway
Telephone: 00353 91 21455   *OS Ref:* M282240   *Operator:* Galway Corporation
Line length: 350yd, circular   *First opened:* 1973

No	Name	Type	Builder	Built
		S/O 2-8-0DH	Severn Lamb	1973

The line runs around the amusement park on the sea front, and sometimes runs well into the evenings.

PICKIE FAMILY FUN PARK RAILWAY

7¼in gauge

Pickie Family Fun Park, Sea front, Bangor, North Down
Telephone: 028 9127 4430   *OS Ref:* J501820
Operator: North Down Borough Council
Line length: 400yd, balloon   *First opened:* 1993

No	Name	Type	Builder	Built
1993	Pickie Puffer	S/O 2-4-2DH	Severn Lamb	1993

The line is a balloon loop with one central station, and a halt at the opposite end where there is a turning wye.

TRAMORE MINIATURE RAILWAY

15in gauge

Fun Park, Sea front, Tramore, County Waterford
Telephone: 00353 51 81403   *OS Ref:* S585012   *Operator:* Tramore Failte Ltd
Line length: 400yd, circular   *First opened:* 1973

No	Name	Type	Builder	Built
		S/O 2-8-0PH	Severn Lamb	1973

This line runs round a fun park, including a boating lake. There are two tunnel/sheds in which the stock is housed at night. During the season operation often continues into the evenings.

WESTPORT HOUSE EXPRESS

15in gauge

Westport House and Children's Zoo, Westport, nr Knock, County Mayo
Telephone: 00353 98 27766   *OS Ref:* L988845   *Operator:* Lord Altamont
Line length: 700yd, balloon   *First opened:* 1990

No	Name	Type	Builder	Built
	W H	S/O 2-6-0DH	Severn Lamb	1989

Trains run from the terminus at Westport Central along a single line and then around a balloon loop next to the lake.

ALDERNEY MINIATURE RAILWAY   7¼in gauge

Mannez Quarry, Alderney, Channel Islands
Telephone: 01481 823260   *OS Ref:* WA601087   *Operator:* M. Taylor
Line length: 400yd, circular   *First opened:* 1995

No	Name	Type	Builder	Built
		0-4-0PH	Roanoke	1999
		0-6-0PH	Maxitrak	1999

The railway follows a scenic route in Mannez Quarry, next to the lighthouse. Operation, at weekends, coincides with the standard gauge trains of the Alderney Railway, from Braye Road.

SAUSMAREZ MANOR MINIATURE
RAILWAY   7¼in gauge

Sausmarez Manor, Sausmarez Road, St Martins, Guernsey, Channel Islands
Telephone: 01481 727256   *OS Ref:* WV329762
Line length: 350yd, circular   *First opened:* 1985   House entry fee

No	Name	Type	Builder	Built
1	Romulus	0-4-0WT	T. Leigh	1987
	Remus	4-4wPH	T. Leigh	1989

This line is an oval with one station and two spurs to sheds.

THE ORCHID LINE   3½in/5in/7¼in gauge

Wildlife Park, Ballaugh, nr Ramsey, Isle of Man
Telephone: 01624 897323   *OS Ref:* SC3767943
Operator: Manx Steam and Model Engineering Club
Website: http://www.homepages.mcb.net/howe/
Line length: 550yd, complex   *First opened:* 1992   Park entry fee

No	Name	Type	Builder	Built
8047	Cushag	0-4-0ST	D. Hill	1987
1366	Florrie	0-6-0PT	D. Hill	1989
	Slieaueyder	0-4-0T	M. Casey	1995
	Jo	0-4-0ST	G. Howe	1997
	Thomas	0-4-0ST	C. Heard	2000

This line can be found within the Wildlife Park at Ballaugh. Trains follow an ingenious course around loops and over crossovers before returning to the station. The track was extended further still over the winter of 1999/2000.

MINIATURE RAILWAYS EXPECTED TO OPEN IN 2000

SHERWOOD FOREST RAILWAY
15in gauge

Sherwood Forest Farm Park, Lamb Pens Farm, Edwinstowe, nr Mansfield, Nottinghamshire NG21 9HL
Telephone: (H): 01623 515339   *OS Ref:* SK586644   *Operators:* D. and C. Colley
Line length: 120yd, end to end   Park entry fee

No	Name	Type	Builder	Built
1		0-4-0ST	K. Hardy	1991
	Pet	0-4-0ST	K. Hardy	1998

This railway is planned to run through two animal enclosures with views over the rare breeds park. The locomotives previously ran on a private railway in Gloucestershire.

The complex layout of the Orchid line, in the Isle of Man, makes it an attractive railway to visit, ride on and photograph, not to mention its unusual rack locomotive Slieaueyder.

The following Model Engineering Societies also have 7¼in gauge ground level and elevated tracks which sometimes open to the public. Generally, these operate less regularly than the locations described in the main part of the book. They are listed alphabetically by county.

England

Bedford Model Engineering Society, Summerfields Fruit Farm, Haynes, Bedford, BEDFORDSHIRE; TL099429.

Pinewood Miniature Railway Society, Pinewood Leisure Centre, Old Wokingham Road, Crowthorne, Wokingham, BERKSHIRE; SU838661.

Bristol Society of Model & Experimental Engineers, Ashton Court Park, BRISTOL; ST554729.

Milton Keynes Model Engineering Society, Kingfisher Country Club, Deanshanger, Milton Keynes, BUCKINGHAMSHIRE; SSP769390.

Cambridge Model Engineering Society, Fulbrooke Road, Newnham, Cambridge, CAMBRIDGESHIRE; TL434572.

Dunhams Wood Light Railway, Rodham Road, March, CAMBRIDGESHIRE; TL443975.

Peterborough Model Engineering Society, Thorpe Hall, Longthorpe, Peterborough, CAMBRIDGESHIRE; TL170986.

Ramsey Miniature Steam Railway Society, Mereside Farm, Ramsey, CAMBRIDGESHIRE.

Chesterfield & District Model Engineering Society, St Peter & Paul School, Hady, Chesterfield, DERBYSHIRE; SK397711.

Plymouth Miniature Steam Locomotive Society, Goodwin Park, Pendeen Crescent, Southway, Plymouth, DEVON; SX491607.

Bournemouth & District Society of Model Engineers, Kings Park, Pokesdown, Bournemouth, DORSET; SZ116928. Elevated track.

Stoford Miniature Locomotive Society, Sensible Motoring Centre, Henstridge, DORSET; ST761217.

South Durham Society of Model Engineers, Hurworth Grange Community Centre, Hurworth, Darlington, DURHAM; NZ297101. Elevated track.

Cleveland Association of Model Engineers, Tees Cottage Pumping Station, Darlington, DURHAM; NZ258139.

Crowborough Locomotive Society, Goldsmiths Leisure Centre, Eridge Road, Crowborough, EAST SUSSEX; TQ521314.

Canvey Railway & Model Engineering Club, Waterside Farm Sports Centre, Canvey Island, ESSEX; TQ781849.

Chelmsford Society of Model Engineers, Meteor Way, Waterhouse Lane, Chelmsford, ESSEX; TL699066.

Rochford Live Steam Group, Freight House, Bradley Way, Rochford, ESSEX; TQ874904.

Saffron Walden & District Model Engineering Society, Audley End Miniature Railway, ESSEX; TL523379. Elevated track.

Chingford & District Model Engineering Club, Ridgeway Park, Chingford, Waltham Forest GREATER LONDON; TQ378937.

Ilford & West Essex Model Railway Club, Chadwell Heath Station, Station Road, Chadwell Heath, Redbridge, GREATER LONDON; TQ477877.

Willesden & West London Society of Model Engineers, Roundwood Park, Willesden, Brent, GREATER LONDON; TQ222842.

Rochdale Society of Model & Experimental Engineers, Springfield Park, Marland, Rochdale, GREATER MANCHESTER; SD875118. Elevated track.

Southampton Society of Model Engineers Ltd, Riverside Park, Bitterne Park, Southampton, HAMPSHIRE; SU437144.

Hereford Society of Model Engineers, Hereford Waterworks Museum, Broomy Hill, HEREFORDSHIRE; SO496392.

Lancaster & Morecambe Model Engineering Society, Cinderbarrow Quarry, nr Carnforth, LANCASHIRE

Westby Miniature Railway Group, Maple Farm Nursery, Peel Hill Bridge, Blackpool, LANCASHIRE; SD363331.

Leicester Society of Model Engineers Ltd, Abbey Park, Leicester, LEICESTERSHIRE; SK584055.

Lincoln & District Model Engineering Society, North Scarle Sports & Social Club, nr Lincoln, LINCOLNSHIRE; SK852668.

Merseyside Live Steam & Model Engineers, Harthill Road, Allerton, Liverpool, MERSEYSIDE; SJ402876.

Barton House Riverside Railway, Hartwell Road, Wroxham, NORFOLK; TG304177.

King's Lynn & District Society of Model Engineers, Lynnsport Leisure Centre, King's Lynn, NORFOLK; TF631211.

Pentney Park Railway, Camping & Caravan Site, Narborough, NORFOLK; TF742141.

Northampton Society of Model Engineers Ltd, Lower Delapre Park, London Road, Northampton, NORTHAMPTONSHIRE; SP756593.

Sandtoft Miniature Railway, Sandtoft Transport Centre, nr Crowle, NORTH LINCOLNSHIRE; SE748082.

Ryedale Society of Model Engineers, The Old School, Gilling East, NORTH YORKSHIRE; SE613770.

Chesterfield & District Model Engineering Society, Papplewick Pumping Station, Ravenshead, NOTTINGHAMSHIRE; SK582521.

City of Oxford Society of Model Engineers, Cutteslowe Park, Cutteslowe, Oxford, OXFORDSHIRE; SP510106.

Yeovil College & District Model Engineering Society, Mudford Recreation Centre, Yeovil, SOMERSET; ST553170.

Rotherham & District Model Engineers Society, Victoria (Rosehill) Park, Rawmarsh, Sheffield, SOUTH YORKSHIRE; SK43X97X.

Sheffield & District Model Engineers, Abbeydale Road South, Dore, Sheffield, SOUTH YORKSHIRE; SK322816.

Sutton Coldfield Model Engineering Society Ltd, Balleny Green, Little Hay, nr Lichfield, STAFFORDSHIRE; SK122027.

Wolverhampton & District Model Engineering Society, Baggeridge Country Park, Wombourne, STAFFORDSHIRE; SO898930.

Teesside Small Gauge Railway Society, Preston Park, Eaglescliffe, STOCKTON-ON-TEES; NZ429161.

Frimley & Ascot Locomotive Club, Frimley Lodge Park, Sturt Road, Frimley, SURREY; SU891560.

Guildford Model Engineering Society, Stoke Park, London Road, Guildford, SURREY; TQ009508.

Malden & District Society of Model Engineers Ltd, Claygate Lane, Thames Ditton, SURREY; TQ162662.

City of Sunderland Model Engineering Society, Roker Park, Roker, Sunderland, TYNE & WEAR; NZ405592. Elevated track.

Echills Wood Railway, National Agricultural Centre, Stoneleigh, WARWICKSHIRE; SP325717.

Rugby Model Engineering Society Ltd, Onley Lane, Rugby, WARWICKSHIRE; SP513727.

Chichester & District Society of Model Engineers Ltd. Bognor Road, Chichester, WEST SUSSEX; SU871047.

Barnsley Society of Model Engineers, Kirklees Light Railway, Clayton West, Kirklees, WEST YORKSHIRE; SE259112. Elevated track.

Brighouse & Halifax Model Engineers, 'Ravensprings', Cawcliffe Road, Brighouse, Calderdale, WEST YORKSHIRE; SE143239.

Spenborough Model Engineers Ltd, Royd Park, Dewsbury Road, Cleckheaton, Kirklees, WEST YORKSHIRE; SE200248.

North Wilts Model Engineering Society, Coate Water Country Park, Swindon, WILTSHIRE; SU179827.

Elmdon Model Engineering Society, Birmingham & Midland Museum of Transport, Wythall, WORCESTERSHIRE; SP072750.

Worcester & District Model Engineering Society, Waverley Street, Cherry Orchard, Worcester, WORCESTERSHIRE; SO852533.

Scotland

Kirkcaldy Model Engineering Society, Beveridge Park, Kirkcaldy, FIFE; NT269911.

Esk Valley Model Engineering Society, Vogrie Country Park, Newtongrange, MIDLOTHIAN; NT377631.

Rolls-Royce Model Engineering Society, Barshaw Park, Glasgow Road, Paisley, RENFREWSHIRE; NS500642. Elevated track.

Wales

Whitchurch (Cardiff) & District Model Engineering Society, Heath Park, Heath, CARDIFF; ST178799.

Wye Valley Railway Society, The Old Station, Tintern, MONMOUTHSHIRE; SO537006.

Mid Wales Model Engineering Society, The Park, Newtown, POWYS; SO106915.

Ireland

Dublin Society of Model & Experimental Engineers, Marlay Park, Ballinteer, Dublin, COUNTY DUBLIN; O152261.

The Rhyl Miniature Railway in operation during August 1999. Simon Townsend

PRIVATE MINIATURE RAILWAYS

The following miniature railway is among those which open to the public on special occasions. Please do not visit this location except on advertised public opening days.

STAPLEFORD MINIATURE RAILWAY
10¼ in gauge

Stapleford Park, Stapleford, nr Melton Mowbray, Leicestershire
OS Ref: SK813182   *Operator:* Friends of the Stapleford Miniature Railway
Website: http://www.fsmr.org.uk
Line length: 1 mile, balloon   *First opened:* 1958

No	Name	Type	Builder	Built
2943	*Hampton Court*	4-6-0	G&SLE/Twining	1939
5565	*Victoria*	4-6-0	Moore/Allcock/Coleby Simkins	1975
752		2-8-4	Coleby Simkins	1971
751	*John H. Gretton*	4-4-2	D. Curwen	1948
D100	*The White Heron*	4w-4wPM	Curwen & Newbery	1962
31192		4-6-2	N. and D. Simkins	1995
6019		4-8-4	J. Wilks	1998

One of the most outstanding 10¼in gauge railways in the UK, the original line was constructed by the late Lord Gretton, and connected with two model passenger-carrying liners on the lake. After the sale of the house, the line was remodelled and is now open to the public only on special days. In 2000 these will be 17/18 June and 27/28 August.

Nos 31192 and 751 climbing the bank from Lakeside, at the Stapleford Miniature Railway, on 25 August 1996. Dave Holroyde

SOCIETIES TO JOIN

The following societies cater particularly for those interested in miniature railways:

Narrow Gauge Railway Society

Annual membership runs from 1 April, subscription currently (2000) £14.50, and includes the journals *Narrow Gauge News* (bi-monthly) and *The Narrow Gauge* (quarterly). Membership Secretary: Lawson Little, 15 Highfields Drive, Old Bilsthorpe, Newark, Nottinghamshire NG22 8SN.

7¼in Gauge Society

Annual membership runs from 1 February, subscription currently (2000) £15, and includes *7¼' Gauge News* journal (quarterly). Membership Secretary: David Everingham, 115 Tom Lane, Sheffield S10 3PE.

Branch Line Society

Annual membership runs from 1 May; there are various subscription rates. *Branch Line News* is published fortnightly and includes a column on Minor Railways. Membership Secretary: Mr J. Holmes, Rose Grove, 23 Church View, Gillingham, Dorset SP8 4XE.

The Heywood Society Journal

Biannual journal devoted to miniature railway subjects. The annual subscription covers the May and October issues each year, currently (1999) £7. Details from: Simon Townsend, 10 Cilnant, Mold, Flintshire CH7 1GG.

A double-headed train is seen passing through the station at the Wortley Top Forge Miniature Railway.
Robin Butterell

INDEX